THE HERO DAD'S INFANT MANUAL

DR. YALE NOGIN

BOOKLOGIX®

Alpharetta, GA

ISBN: 978-1-61005-913-8

Library of Congress Control Number: 2017910366

10 9 8 7 6 5 4 3 2   1 1 1 4 1 7

Printed in the United States of America

♾This paper meets the requirements of ANSI/NISO Z39.48-1992 (Permanence of Paper)

Illustrations by Matthew Scott Cohen

DEDICATION

For my co-sheriff Michelle,
thank you for being my true companion.
For my children,
Eliana, Jonah, Sarah, and Lila,
thank you for being sturdy.
I love you all more than the stars in the night sky.

If one advances confidently in the direction of his dreams, and endeavors to live the life which he has imagined, he will meet with a success unexpected in common hours.

—Henry David Thoreau

CONTENTS

PREFACE

Thank you for reading *The Hero Dad's Infant Manual*!
Heaven knows we need more Hero Dads walking
around today more than ever. It would have been fun
meeting you in one of my infant manual classes. It
is nice to have the opportunity to connect in person,
because discussing your transition into fatherhood
and becoming a dad is personal.

I chose to name my class and this manual *The Hero
Dad's Infant Manual* because unlike the fictional heroes
that we all love, you, my friend, have real powers,
which your child will love. You have the power to
support your partner through the birth of your baby,
power to soothe and care for your new baby, and the
ultimate power to choose to engage and create a solid,
loving, safe home and family life, and a fathering and

husbanding "with baby version" experience that will give your child a solid foundation that will empower the course of their life.

Being a Hero Dad does not mean you will be a perfect dad. As a matter of fact, a Hero Dad makes plenty of mistakes. What a Hero Dad does that is different than the zero dads walking around is that he makes the effort to be the best he can be for his family. He tries his best, makes mistakes, gets back up, and tries again. He is conscious that he will need to constantly grow as a person to overcome the challenges that inherently come with being a parent and partner who is raising a child, and he rises to the challenge.

You having power, growing, and facing challenges may sound like the theme of a fun hero movie, but I assure you—fatherhood is not a joke. Fatherhood is the hardest job I have ever had, and I am not a stranger to hard work. My hope is that this book makes your transition an easier one and that the insights you will learn help you to realize your best fathering experience and to create a happy home. Helping people to be happier is what I wanted to do from the time I was a small kid working in my parent's grocery store. I can't honestly explain why I have always wanted to assist my fellow person; I just have. That may sound silly but it is true.

I truly would love to help you become the Hero Dad in your home, but you will need to put in the effort. There is real happiness to be had in working together with your partner to create and maintain a stable, safe, loving family and home life. Being the Hero Dad is a choice you make every day.

ACKNOWLEDGMENTS

First and foremost, thank you Michelle for loving me and liking me just the way I am, and for always helping me to be the best I can be. I am so glad to be traveling on this wild ride of marriage, friendship, parenthood, personal growth, and maturity with you.

Mom and marvelous Marvin, thank you for all your encouragement, support, and generosity in bringing The Hero Dad™ to fruition. You have enabled me to help improve the fathering experience of men everywhere. I love you and appreciate you every day.

Thank you, Dad, forever watching over me, for always walking the walk, and for showing me that a man can be nice and tough as well as a loving, involved husband and father.

Thank you, Matthew Scott Cohen (www.Mat-thewScottCohen.com), for being an amazing, talented artist and for helping me bring The Hero Dad to life. You are a real pleasure to work with, and I appreciate all your effort and attention to details. To all the amazing folks at BookLogix who helped me through the process of creating *The Hero Dad's Infant Manual*, thank you for your patience and guidance through this publishing process.

Eliana, Jonah, Sarah, and Lila, I never would have imagined exactly how much time, effort, self-awareness, self-discipline, and maturity it would take to raise you, my children. Balancing being your guide, teacher, friend, cook, and general manager—while maintaining a healthy relationship with your mother and taking care of myself—has been my most challenging work to date. Thank you for being a catalyst for my growth into the man and father I am today. Know this: you are worth the effort. When you one day experience parenthood (God willing), you will understand the love I feel for each of you.

And finally, thank you to all my dear friends and past students who have given me amazing, positive feedback. You have always supported me in believing that if more men had the tools, they would create healthier and more peaceful homes to live happier lives in.

INTRODUCTION

Congratulations for being a man about to have a baby! Being a dad is an amazing experience and really a privilege, my friend. If you think about it, not all men get the opportunity to be a father, to be someone's dad, to join the ranks of men who get to walk around knowing you have participated in creating a most amazing miracle—a miracle that will fill you with pride and joy, and sometimes make you say, "What were we thinking having kids?!" You have successfully captured the heart of a woman or partner, one who thinks enough of you to carry your bloodline on to another generation, which is a huge deal! You should be extremely proud. Again, congratulations!

My name is Yale Nogin, and for the past fourteen years and counting I've been preparing new dads and new dads-to-be like you for the adventure, challenge, and privilege of being a new father. When you first shared with your friends and family that you're going to have a baby, you probably did not find yourself with a shortage of advice on what to do and how to do it. Here you will receive more than advice. You will receive actual tools that will work every time you pull them out of your tool bag, all of which are designed to increase your odds of becoming the Hero Dad you have always wanted to be.

THE TOOLS AND PERSPECTIVES YOU ARE ABOUT TO LEARN HAVE BEEN PUT THROUGH THE PACES. THEY WORK.

You are getting the benefit of learning from all of the mistakes that came from surviving my four babies. These tools were started with our first, Eliana; improved upon with our second, our son, Jonah; added to with our third, Sarah; and mastered with our fourth, Lila.

I am wearing my heart on my sleeve, presenting you a true labor of love to help you realize your best fathering experience, cut your learning curve at the tasks at hand, and most importantly increase your odds of maintaining a happy, healthy marriage in the process.

You know how parents say that they wish they had a manual on how to figure out what to do with their new baby? This is it. This is the manual that will help you get from pre-birth through your first year and way beyond.

If you went to my class in the hospital in the past fourteen years, you, like most men, would have stayed at least an extra hour to learn as many tools as you could—that is, before your pregnant wife would call to let you know it was time to come home. This is one of the main reasons for taking on the task of creating the Hero Dad online class and book for you: to share all of the tools, without being rushed and without leaving anything out.

The other reason the Hero Dad is a reality is because other dads-to-be like you shared with me that the tools that they gained left them feeling more confident and ready to face their upcoming journey while having a fun time learning. If more men aquired these tools, then more men would feel better prepared for the job ahead.

For these reasons—and that your partner was incredibly intelligent enough to purchase this book for you—the Hero Dad is a reality.

You may be feeling nervous. You may have never even held a baby before, or changed a diaper. That's okay. You may be feeling totally cool and just want some helpful tools to make your experience smoother. That's okay. You may be freaking out, questioning if you're even cut out for the job—that's okay also.

My friend, everything is going to be okay. One last time: everything is going to be okay. And if you are making the effort to read this book, you will be better than okay.

How do I know everything is going to be okay? The truth is, there are no guarantees, only odds; however, this class will provide you tools that, if you use them, your odds that everything will be okay will dramatically increase.

The tools that you are about to learn have successfully navigated me and my wife through the infant and toddler phase of raising a child four times without any major casualties. Okay, okay—a couple minor casualties along the way, but no major ones. We've all made it to the next phase together.

Do you remember how Clark Kent was able to take ownership of his powers after he received the tools to do so from Jor-El? You may not be Superman, and I may not be Jor-El; however, if you pay attention and engage with these tools and instructions, you will feel empowered to be the Hero Dad that you want to be for your family and that your partner is expecting and hoping you will be! No pressure, though.

Without any further ado, let's get to it.

CHAPTER 1

PRE-BIRTH TOOLS

DURING pregnancy, you may feel that there's not much you can do to help the process. Up to this point, your wife has been carrying the load (pun intended), and there hasn't been much for you to do except be supportive and maybe do a little painting. But just because your baby isn't here yet doesn't mean you can't get a head start on being a Hero Dad. These Pre-Birth Tools will help make your mom-to-be happier and more comfortable, and they will make her job as a Hero Mom that much easier while improving her confidence in you.

Your first Pre-Birth Tool will prove extremely useful to your lady before your new addition arrives; if you embrace it, it will also prove useful afterward and throughout your marriage. Your first Pre-Birth Tool is massage.

Now you might be thinking to yourself, *I am not really a touchy-feely type of guy. I've never really done a massage. I don't know how to do that.*

MY FRIEND, IT IS TIME FOR YOU TO LEARN SOME BASIC MASSAGE TOOLS, AND THIS IS WHY: HAPPY HUSBANDS KNOW YOU MUST FIRST GIVE IF YOU WANT TO RECEIVE. WHY NOT INITIATE A GESTURE LIKE A SIMPLE MASSAGE THAT IS WITHIN YOUR POWER, EASY TO DO, WILL HELP HER FEEL BETTER, AND ONLY COSTS YOU YOUR EFFORT?

Let's talk basic anatomy here. Your wife is carrying around the weight of a big bowling ball in her belly that she did not carry around before. The weight of your baby puts a lot of pressure on her lower back—a lot of pressure that you are partially responsible for putting there.

Your wife is likely experiencing some back pain and tension. A massage can help alleviate some of that pain and tension and is extremely easy to do. You do not need to be a master masseuse to help her through the pre-birth phase; you only need to want to help her feel better. Here are two simple techniques for you to use

that always worked for my wife, Michelle. You can be on the bed or carpet, wherever she is most comfortable. Have your mom-to-be position herself in what's known in yoga as Child's Pose. It's easy: Put a pillow or two in front of her on the floor and have her sit on her heels with her knees apart.

Then simply have her lean over the pillows, resting her belly down. This should be a really comfortable position—it was for Michelle. After your wife is comfortably in Child's Pose, sit behind her. Take your thumbs and rub them up and down right next to her spine—these are the muscles that are under a lot of tension and doing a lot of work.

 You want to rub up and down the lower back, starting above her tush. You can move to the upper back as well. Use pressure that's comfortable for her, and if you're not sure, just ask. "How is this pressure, honey? Too much? Too little?"

CHECKING IN IS COMMUNICATING, WHICH IS WHAT YOU WANT TO BE DOING AS MUCH AS POSSIBLE.

Don't worry if your thumbs get tired—you're going to build some stamina. In the meantime, you can also use the palms of your hands. Between your thumbs and your palms, you will have a happy lady on your hands! Pun intended.

Another nice massage technique is to have her sit between your legs. Again, you can be on your bed or on the floor, wherever you are both comfortable. Prop some pillows up behind you. She can lean forward over some pillows if it is comfortable for her, or you can have her lean back on your chest; sometimes it is

more comfortable to have a pillow between you and her.

Wrap your hands over her shoulders and move your thumbs around, up, and down. Just follow the outline of her neck and shoulders, and that's it! You don't need to be fancy.

The key to a good massage is simply wanting to help—that's what will make it work. If you genuinely want to reduce her stress, that message will come through and she'll want to return the favor. These easy massage techniques will help her physically be more comfortable, which will help her emotionally to feel happier and more connected to you and thinking that she is with her own hero!

Now, massage is a multipurpose tool. Not only will a massage 100 percent help your significant other feel better before birth; it will also 100 percent help her feel better after the birth, which will help you. Let me explain . . .

ROMANCE IS A BIG PART OF MAINTAINING A HEALTHY MARRIAGE, WHICH IS A BIG PART OF RAISING HEALTHY KIDS.

This Massage Tool is excellent for postbirth, not only to help Mom relax, but also to help you bridge the gap when it's time to add some romance back into your lives. You may be looking at your wife two and a half, three months in—maybe sooner, maybe later. She's looking good, and you know what? She's had a stressful day. Your baby just started sleeping through the night, but she's not sleeping through the night yet. Your Hero Mom is feeling pretty good, but is still under a little bit of stress. She might be willing to get romantic, but may need a little convincing. When you offer her a massage, do you think she is going to say, "NO, that is a terrible idea"? Or do you think she may say, "Thank you, honey, that is a great idea"? Odds are you will get the "Great idea, honey!" response.

Bring your partner between your legs, give her a hug, share with her how much you love her, wrap your hands over her shoulders, and massage them. After she's relaxed and purring like a kitten, give a couple kisses on the neck . . . If your heart is in the right place, you know what happens next—I don't need to spell it out.

Keep in mind, though—life is stressful after your baby is born even when everything is going well. Even though the doctor may have said she is physiologically healed and healthy, you won't be getting back into the sack until your significant other is emotionally ready for that to happen. When the time is right (which we will cover in detail in Chapter 11: Sex and Relationships), you'll find that the Massage Tool is excellent to help ease some stress during the first couple months after your baby is born and through your marriage, because as you will soon find out, every phase of raising children offers a level of stress.

Your second tool is another one that is fantastic both pre- and post-birth: a nice, deep breath.

THAT'S RIGHT—A NICE, DEEP BREATH.

Now you may be thinking, *Right on! A deep breath, that's cool.* You may also be thinking, *Gimme a break. This is BS and won't do anything for me.* But a couple of weeks after your baby is born, the clock will read something like three thirty or four o'clock in the morning. You didn't sleep the night before, it will be your turn to feed the baby, she will be crying, you will exhaust every effort to soothe her. Of course, with the tools you are learning here you will be way ahead of the game, but let's just say there are going to be some nights that will bring you to the end of your rope. The only thing you can do is remember to take a nice, deep breath. Sometimes you may need to take three or four, even five deep breaths. When you do, it will help you to calm down and refocus so that you can take care of business without losing yourself or getting upset with the baby, which is never good.

It's beneficial to practice in order to remember to use the deep breath, especially if you're not in the habit. Taking a deep breath is a multipurpose tool. It can help you when the baby is born, and it also can help you at work, at play, and if you're feeling stressed out or overwhelmed. If you stop, just stop for a second and take a nice, deep breath; it will prove to be most beneficial for you. Taking a deep breath brings fresh oxygen to your system, which I hear is helpful, and a conscious deep breath can also help reset your operating system, so to speak. Try it now—seriously. No matter where you are, you can practice. Breathing in and out through your nose is more energizing, and in through your nose and out through your mouth is more relaxing.

The next Pre-Birth Tool is by far one of my favorites to help you reach hero status, and that is the Food Prep–Hero Tool. Depending on how much time you have left before your baby arrives, you'll want to put this tool into play right away.

What exactly is the Food Prep–Hero Tool? Think about this: you get home with your new baby. You're excited, you unpack, everyone settles in, and then you will realize it's seven o'clock at night and your team is hungry. Everyone is going to be hungry and tired, yet the only one of you that will be taken care of in the food department is going to be your baby. Enter the Food Prep–Hero Tool. For the first couple of weeks and maybe even months, everyone is going to be exhausted at the end of the day, especially if one of you is going back to work. You know you're going to be at your limit, so food could be an issue if you don't take care of business. You might have somebody over to help with the cooking. However, you may not have that good fortune.

This tool will work for you whether or not you know how to cook. If you want to be a hero, this is what you do. First, let's talk about how to become a Food-Prep Hero if you do like to cook. I also like to cook, so this is what I did: I made food that we like to eat and I froze it. If you have a little bit of time before the baby comes, cook up some of your favorite foods and freeze them. Now, not all foods freeze very well; however, a lot of them do. I learned about freezing food from my mom, Roz. We used to laugh at how she froze everything, but now we would be lost without the freezer. As she knew from experience, having food that's ready to go makes life much easier.

For example, if you're not a vegetarian, chicken cutlets are great to cook and freeze. You can grill or parboil (partially cooking chicken in water or chicken broth) a few dozen cutlets, let them cool off, and then put them in freezer bags, label and date them, and put them in the freezer. You can defrost them in the microwave in a few minutes and create a meal quickly, leaving you good to go. Chicken cutlets are awesome because they are a versatile protein that help you create so many meals. You can put them on a sandwich with lettuce and tomato. You can chop them up with celery, peppers, and scallions, add some mayo and make chicken salad. You can add some red or marinara sauce and cheese and make chicken parmesan, or throw them in a salad—the possibilities are endless and easy. Other good foods that freeze well are lasagna, baked ziti, and meatballs. With our last baby, Lila, I cooked up a roast beef, sliced it up with some gravy in portion-sized bags, and threw them in the freezer. Delicious and easy, easy, easy. Decide what you want for dinner, and when five o'clock rolls around and everyone is getting hungry, all you have to do is throw it in the oven or microwave to defrost, and bingo! You are the hero for saving the day. You also can parboil cutlets and put them in a Tupperware in the fridge for up to a week for easy meals, and you can preserve the broth for soup!

Casseroles are also great to cure cravings. They freeze well, and are versatile because you can go vegetarian or carnivore and you will usually have leftovers. With casseroles, consider cooking them halfway if you plan on freezing them, and let them cool before freezing. You can also use throw away tins to eliminate cleanup. You can check out my "How to Make Baked Ziti" video at www.TheHeroDad.com.

If you don't like or know how to cook, this is what you do. Go to the frozen-food section of your local grocery store and you will find a variety of prepared foods and vegetables. These days there are many, many choices that are on the pretty healthy side. Many brands offer one-skillet meals that have a protein, a carb, and vegetables with some kind of sauce, and they cook up in just ten to fifteen minutes! You will find ones with rice, with pastas, with chicken, beef, or fish—there are all kinds that you can get. I cook most of the time; however, there are some nights that I'm just beat at the end of the day, and it's nice to be able to fall back on skillet meals.

Here is how you can turn this Hero Tool into a Super Hero Tool. To make one of those skillet meals even better for your family, after you put the meal into the skillet, add an extra bag of frozen vegetables! You can use whatever kind you like, or you can look on the bag and see what vegetables are already in the meal and add an extra bag of those because you know they will "go" with the meal. If you opt to add the extra veggies, throw them into the pot at the same time you put the skillet meal in to cook. There is always a lot of sauce, so it will coat the meal and the extra vegetables, and it's absolutely delicious. You'll get more nutrients, more fiber, more veggies, plus it may even stretch the meal, which is excellent for your family. And, if you make two bags of the skillet meals, your team will be set up for lunch the next day. One super easy, super way to be a major hero: have dinner covered! You can see how easy it is on the "How to Make a Skillet Meal" video at www.TheHeroDad.com.

THEHERODAD.COM/RESOURCES

There are also a few other tools that can help your family in the food department. There are many neighborhood, church, and social groups that hook up families when they have babies by paying meals forward. For example, for our last two babies, people in our neighborhood group knew we were expecting. Folks in the neighborhood signed up and everybody contributed one meal. You can eat for ten days some-times by these meals that people pay forward. Then, of course, when one of your neighbors is having a baby, it's your turn to pay it forward to them. If you belong to or join a group like this, it is very nice.

Your next Pre-Birth Tool is the Game-Plan Tool. My dad, Jerry, used to say all the time that "A smart man plans one day in advance." He believed that people are too caught up in today to think about the future.

HEROES ARE PREPARED, YET MOST OF US TEND NOT TO THINK MUCH PAST OUR BABY BEING BORN—THAT IS WHY YOU CAN SHINE BY THINKING AHEAD.

Start thinking about or even writing down any events that you know or think may happen when you get home from the hospital. That way, you can be better prepared.

Let's talk about some events that could happen in your world within the first month or so. Are you having friends at the house when you get back? A wel-come-home party for the baby, or maybe a last baby shower? Or do you want no one at the house when you get back so you and Mom can bond with your baby? I know a few guys who left special messages on their voicemail: "Hi everyone, little Johnny is eight pounds and healthy! Thanks so much for your call, and we will call you back in a week or so after we bond with the baby." What do you guys want to do? What's your plan for after you get home?

What can you do to help prepare now for one of those events? Are you Jewish and having a bris in eight days at your home or someplace else? Do you have your mohel (you know, the rabbi who makes the snip) on speed dial? Those kinds of details are good to be thinking about. Do you have in-laws, or are your parents coming to visit or stay with you? Are you excited about the visit? If not, what is your plan?

The topic of houseguests comes up in almost every one of my classes. Best-case scenario: You love your in-laws, your parents are great, and there are no issues whatsoever. In that case, you just need to let everyone know when to come, or help figure out where everyone is going to stay while they visit.

But what if the parental figure or figures are, shall we say, overbearing? There are a few schools of thought on how to deal with this. Whether it's your parent or your partner's parent, the number-one thing to realize is that it's probably not a secret. Is it a source of contention between you and your partner? At this point, you and your partner have hopefully discussed the overbearing parent that will be there and if not, it is a good time to do so in order to make a game plan together to deal with that person in the best possible manner. One school of thought is to just keep your mouth shut; grin and bear it until they are gone.

THE OTHER SCHOOL OF THOUGHT, WHICH IS THE MOST BENEFICIAL IN THE LONG RUN, IS COMING TOGETHER WITH YOUR PARTNER TO ADDRESS THE ISSUES UP FRONT.

Set some ground rules for what is and isn't okay for them to do around the baby. Communicating with our parents is definitely easier said than done. But if the folks coming to visit irritate you guys or cause extra stress and you do not set up ground rules, it will happen every time they come. Figure out a game plan on how to deliver the boundaries in a nice way.

REMEMBER, YOU DON'T HAVE TO BE MEAN ABOUT ANYTHING—IT'S JUST A CONVERSATION. IF YOU COME TOGETHER WITH YOUR SPOUSE TO DEAL WITH THIS KIND OF ISSUE, YOU'LL FIND THAT YOU WILL BE HAPPY THAT YOU MADE THE STAND.

This could be a good Mommy and Daddy family-bonding experience.

THE KEY HERE IS COMING TOGETHER AND COMMUNICATING.

At every turn, there will be opportunities to bond even closer with your spouse. If you come together with your partner, figure out some boundaries you'd like to see in place and are brave enough to talk it out with your parental figures, you will feel enlightened and grown up. You will be taking an active role in creating the new routines around raising your baby and for your new nuclear family.

When you set ground rules in a kind but firm way, things tend to work out so much more nicely. There's less stress and tension around the baby when they come to visit. You will find that grandparents are not easy to change and probably won't comply 100 percent, but know this—they want to be around their grandbaby, and that is a big motivator to chill and get with your program if they need to.

Next is a little gold-nugget Hero Tool for you: the Paternity-Leave Tool. This tool is a gem. Depending on your employer, the standard paternity leave gives you approximately two weeks off with your family. If you have control over the timing that you can take off and want to turn those two weeks into pure gold, here's what you do: Take off one week when the baby is due, and take your second week off a month after your baby is born. That first week, everything is so exciting and fun. Everyone is celebrating and you get to bond and start getting to know your baby. That first week is important for sure! Want to know when it would be even more important to have a week at home? You got it: In a month, when there are no more parties, when the sleep deprivation is setting in, when all of your friends go back to their regular lives. That is when your partner will truly appreciate your presence at home. You will have that week to really reconnect with your new family and help your Hero Mom, who will be even more fried than you are.

BEING THERE WHEN THE EXCITEMENT HAS WORN OFF AND YOU ARE TRANSITIONING INTO NEW DAY-TO-DAY ROUTINES WILL HELP HER GET THROUGH THE END OF THE BABY BLUES AND MAKE A HUGE DIFFERENCE FOR MORALE OF THE HOME TEAM.

So, if you have control over the time you take off and do it that way, you, my friend, will be a hero once again.

The next Pre-Birth Tool is knowing your options if your baby is breech. If your baby is breech, it means her head is up instead of down past the point when she "should" have flipped. Approximately 3 to 4 percent of babies are head up at full term, which is not the ideal way for them to be delivered.[1] Our first baby, Eliana, was breech, and because she was our first baby and we didn't know what was going on, we didn't take action until late in the game (around thirty-five weeks).

---

1 "Breech Birth: What It Means for You," What to Expect, last updated March 23, 2015, http://www.whattoexpect.com/pregnancy/breech-baby/.

Michelle was complaining of the baby dancing on her bladder all the time, but we thought the baby would flip naturally if she had a little more time. We were expecting everything to go just right, and we passed the date when the baby should have flipped over and gotten into position, between approximately thirty and thirty-four weeks.

Michelle absolutely wanted to have a natural, vaginal birth, but sometimes if the baby won't flip, the mother can end up needing a C-section. So, we looked into all our different options at that time. We found there were two main options that we could try. The first one is an external version, which is a technique administered by an OB. The second is called the Webster technique and is primarily used by chiropractors.

We heard some horror stories about the external version and decided to try the Webster technique first. The Webster technique is usually successful if caught in time. If your baby is breech and you are inclined to try the Webster technique, look for a family chiropractic office. I like asking friends for recommendations; however, if you were just picking one from a list, look for a family practice as opposed to a sports-specific office and ask if they have a Webster-certified doctor there. The Webster technique balances out the muscles and ligaments of the pelvis in just the right way to help create the correct environment for the baby to flip. We did try it, but we believe it did not work because it was too late in the game. We should've started earlier, maybe in the twenty-five-week range, but we just believed that the baby would flip.

We wanted to make every effort for Michelle to have a vaginal birth, so we opted to try the external version. We did a little research, and a couple of people that we talked to had unpleasant experiences with the external version. Some of them were left with black-and-blue marks; some of them it didn't work for; some said it was painful. We decided to give it a shot anyway. We found that it was a pleasant experience, and it worked for us. This is how it went.

We showed up at the hospital and we were put in an exam room. The nurse gave Michelle a muscle relaxer so she could chill out a little bit. Then, after about fifteen or twenty minutes, they gave her one more muscle relaxer while we waited for the doctor to show up. It was early in the morning, and when the doctor arrived, he wasn't in scrubs but his office clothes. I remember he was wearing a nice sports jacket and tie, which surprised me. He rolled up his sleeves, positioned his hands toward the baby's head, and directed the nurse toward the baby's bottom. Then they pushed and the baby flipped over. It was almost like the *Alien* movie, when you can see the monster moving inside—it was cool.

The external version worked fantastically, so we definitely say it's worth a try. In our experience, it was positive and worked with relative ease. So, if your baby is breech and you are concerned about having a vaginal birth, definitely try all your options. The Webster gets great results if you are on the ball; however, the external version worked for us and I'd recommend it for sure.

There is another resource you should be aware of and that is "Spinning Babies: Easier birth with fetal positioning" (http://spinningbabies.com/). The Spinning Babies program uses techniques that use balance, gravity, and movement early on and through pregnancy to help ensure your baby is in its best position for the easiest and safest position to be delivered.

Now for your last Pre-Birth Tool: communication. Let me share with you a big secret about having a baby.

A baby is not so hard to manage. If you, Lord willing, have a child without health issues, then, that's right— I'm saying a baby is not so hard to manage, especially with your new tools. Changing poopy diapers, feeding and burping your baby, changing his outfits, holding and rocking him, singing to him, and doing all the tasks you will do to manage his survival is not the hard part.

The hard part is that your life and all of your routines that you and your partner have grown to know are about to change. It is the changing world around you that's stressful, not the baby itself. Sure, you need to learn some new tasks. However, your ability to communicate what's going on with you in your head and heart and your ability to hear what is going on with your partner will be what helps you stay grounded and grow together through these initial changes. Communication is what will set you up for success.

Your last Hero Tool here is one that my dad, Jerry, passed on to me, and it has helped me several times. He shared with me that as life changes and you work toward melding your two ideas of how you want your lives to be and how you want to raise your child together, sometimes you will argue. That is normal. You both grew up in different homes with different childhood experiences that will be influencing you both. When and if that happens, remember these two tools. First, you should never leave your bedroom. Choose to stay. Never go sleep on the couch or in another room — do not leave your room. Stay there and work it out the best you can, or turn over and go to sleep, but don't ever leave. By choosing to stay, you're saying you're not going anywhere. You're going to work things out. Even if things get heated, having your partner know you are not going anywhere, that you are staying no matter what, is a powerful message.

Second, if you are having a heated discussion and you don't feel heard, you may feel like you're not being understood. Even though you may be upset or angry, be the hero and rise above the situation, close your lips, and just let her talk. You may be furious; however, if you can remember to take a breath, close your lips, and sit down, you're halfway there. Seek to understand before you are understood, and odds are you will have an easier time working things out. Why should you have to be the one to rise above the situation? Why not? Why not take the opportunity so many men leave on the table to just stop and listen to understand and put your partner first? I am not saying here to roll over and forget your point of view—I am saying that listening to and understanding your partner will help get you to a solution more easily and with less yelling, which makes for a less stressful home.

 **FUNNY—TO COMMUNICATE, SOMETIMES YOU DO NOT HAVE TO SAY ANYTHING AT ALL.**

Hopefully you won't find yourself in the middle of too many heated arguments. However, it does happen. These tools have helped me many times and if you need them, they will work for you. Having clear, honest communication will help you to create the solid foundation to raise your family on.

And speaking of communication, just you wait and see what your wife is going to "communicate" clearly and honestly to you as she is pushing your baby out! You'll hear all about it in the next chapter.

CHAPTER 2

YOUR BIRTH EXPERIENCE

HERE it comes: the good, the bad, and the ugly. We are going to cover all the different aspects of your birth experience, from getting ready to go to what kind of clothes to pack. Vaginal birth, planned C-sections, and emergency C-sections will all be covered. We will also cover the use of doulas, midwives versus OBs, circumcision, cord blood, and several other topics that are sure to come up during your birth experience.

PLEASE DO NOT BE OVERWHELMED. YOU DO NOT NEED TO BE AN EXPERT IN ANY OF THESE AREAS.

You only need to have a good, working idea of what is going on in general, because unless you are delivering your baby by yourself in your home without anyone helping, you will have professional people around you who will do the heavy lifting during your birth experience. The purpose of this chapter is to prepare you for most of the different possible scenarios you may encounter within a relatively normal, healthy birth experience. Although there are plenty of Pre-Birth Tools you can put into play, during the actual birth, you are mostly a support person, and your real work as Daddy will officially start when your baby is delivered.

Let's get rolling with what to bring to the hospital. There are lists and lists on what to bring for Mom, but this is about you, Dad, so don't forget to pack yourself a bag! With a typical, healthy, vaginal birth in a hospital, you're looking at two nights away from home. If you're having a C-section, you're looking at a minimum of four days to a week, depending on your insurance and whether there are any complications during the birth. If you are delivering at a birth center, you will usually be back home six to eight hours after your baby is born. You want to make sure you have enough clothes to get you through your stay. Hospital delivery rooms are typically on the colder side, so think long-sleeved, cotton T-shirts and some layers. You want to be warm, and you can always take off layers. You should also think comfort when it comes to the delivery and hospital stay because the process could take a while. Our first delivery took eighteen hours from start to finish!

You should also consider putting a snack pack together. Depending on your hospital, there might be a fast-food chain in there. Our hospital here in Atlanta has one and that's great. You, as well as I, have probably never had a bad Big Mac; however, fast food gets old quickly, as does having to keep paying out of pocket. My recommendation is to pack some snacks that you like to eat and have them ready to go with your other bags. Snacks mean something different to all of us, but you may want to stick with food that is quick and easy. Whether that means potato chips or pretzels, or a couple of protein bars, nuts, dried fruit, six pack . . . of water—whatever you want—bring it so you have some food to nosh on during the labor. Your wife could be in labor like mine was for a whole day, and you want to be able to stay in the room as much as possible. If you're a great planner, you may even manage to bring some sandwiches in a cooler!

It is a great idea to have both your bags and snacks ready to go at least two weeks before her due date so you are prepared for when you get "the call" that it is show time! Let's talk about "show time" for a minute. Braxton-Hicks contractions, or "false labor pains," are irregular contractions that can start midway through pregnancy and get more frequent closer to your birth date. Braxton-Hicks contractions are pretty painful. What do you do when your wife is close to her due date and you are both unsure whether she is having Braxton-Hicks contractions or if she is actually in labor? The pain of the contractions can be especially significant if this is your first birth experience and you cannot yet compare them to actual baby-coming-out contractions. If she wants to go for a hospital run, but the contractions aren't quite close enough where they would be for her to be dilating and in labor, my advice is to go! Contractions can be confusing with how far apart and which contractions mean what. Think of it like this: the farther from the time of birth, the farther apart the contractions. During the first stage of labor, you are looking at contractions every fifteen to twenty minutes, and then they get closer and more intense as her cervix dilates and she gets closer to the actual time.[2] She will need to push at ten centimeters.

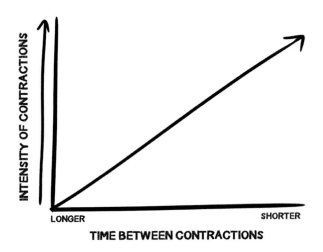

Many couples take a run to the hospital, only to have the doctor say, "You're not really ready," and send them back home. If you talk to experienced parents, most will say that you want to be at home as long as

<hr>

2 "Pregnancy and the Stages of Labor and Childbirth," WebMD, accessed December 5, 2016, http://www.webmd.com/baby/guide/pregnancy-stages-labor#1.

possible. But with your first birth, sometimes you just aren't feeling quite confident enough to know whether or not these are real contractions. It is not an exact science—usually Braxton-Hicks contractions will be localized to her belly, and can start even a few weeks before her due date. Real contractions will typically wrap all the way around her waist from the back to the front. If everything is going well, you have not had any complications, and you are both feeling good and confident, then you could recommend that she take a warm bath to relax her contracted tummy and muscles. If she is having Braxton-Hicks contractions and her water has not broken, then a nice, warm bath can really help to relax her muscles.

If she is having Braxton-Hicks contractions, you're not quite sure if they're real, and she wants you to take her the hospital, just go! Worst-case scenario, you will have a fun story to tell about when you thought it was time, went to the hospital, and ended up in a diner eating french fries instead of delivering the baby. Whatever your story will be, it will be a good one.

Another thing to consider in the time leading up to your arrival at the hospital is where she will be when her water breaks. It does not always happen like in the movies. Sometimes a woman's water doesn't even break. In our four pregnancies, Michelle's water never broke; they had to break it in the hospital with a crochet hook–looking thing. We were past her due date and her contractions were becoming more consistent and coming closer together, steadily around three to five minutes apart, and were really painful. The water isn't always necessarily going to break.

So here is your second tool, if you don't have one already: a waterproof cover for your mattress. Depending on how far along you are, if your partner's water breaks on your mattress, goodbye mattress! It will be ruined because her "water" is not really "water." If you're a month or two away from delivery, consider getting one of those waterproof mattress covers. The twenty-dollar waterproof cover could save you a couple thousand on a mattress. Just trying to save you some money here!

Many men have expressed concerns to me about how long you have to get to the hospital after the water breaks. Some guys are looking for a good excuse to speed to the hospital like in the movies. If your partner's water breaks, it is not usually an emergency, but it does mean you need to get your act together. If your partner's water actually breaks or she perceives it to have broken because she feels like she is wet and did not pee, call your delivering OB or midwife, because every birth and pregnancy is different and your delivering profes-

sional will let you know what you need to do. Again, you do not need to be the expert here; just call and find out what to do. The takeaway here is that under normal circumstances her water breaking is not an emergency, so please do not drive crazy to your birth place. Be careful; getting into an accident is not the way you want to get the party started. You want to take action and make the call, because once her water breaks she is open to infection, and the baby usually will be coming sooner than later. However, you do have time to be careful and get to where you are going safely.

Another thing to think about in the time you are getting ready to go to the hospital is if you are preregistered at the hospital. When our partners go to the OB or their midwife—whoever is delivering your baby—preregistering and taking a birth-place tour are topics that come up, and the Hero Mom typically takes care of it. However, asking, "Hon, are we preregistered?" shows interest in the process that makes you look good, so ask her! Being preregistered is a good thing. Taking care of it will mean taking care of less paperwork at the hospital. When you show up for the party and it is show time, extra paperwork is not what either of you will want to be doing. You will have enough on your mind when filling out the remainder of the paperwork that was not covered in preregistration and getting back into a room.

Okay, so let's just say for argument's sake that you are close to, at, or past your due date, and her contractions are coming fast and furious—meaning they are three to five minutes apart or closer and last close to or over a minute—her water may or may not have broken, and she is feeling ready to go to the hospital. You get her bag if it's not in the car already, you get your bag that you packed for yourself, and maybe get your snack pack or cooler. You get into your car and you head to the hospital. Let's say she's in the car and it's too late—the baby is coming. What do you do?

You do what men have done for years and years and years. You pull over to the side of the road, call 911 if you have a phone, and they will walk you through the process.

It happened right here in our town not too long ago on the side of Georgia 400. The baby was coming and the dad had to take care of business right there in the back of his Chevy. I had a friend of that dad in my class who was scared that he would have to deliver his baby by himself because he was close to his buddy's experience. His buddy was able to deliver his baby and if in the same circumstance, the dad-to-be, who was in my class, could have made it happen as well. If you find yourself in that position, you just want to remember counterpressure, meaning as your baby is coming out of the birth canal, once his shoulders pass through, he will pop out! Counterpressure is applying gentle pressure to your baby's head to ease him out and to prevent him from popping out. With our last baby, I asked Michelle what she thought of me delivering the baby myself. Of course, she told me I was CRAZY—it was not going to happen! Although I totally could do it. Right? And so could you—you totally could do it if you had to.

Now, under ideal circumstances, you make it to the hospital without having to deliver the baby. You check in, and at this point you will hang out with the other people waiting in the lobby—congratulations, small talk, small talk, blah, blah, blah—until they have your room ready for you. Back in your delivery room, they will put a gown on your mom-to-be, as well as some baby monitors—one for Mom, one for baby.

Once she is in bed, the nurse will ask her if she wants an enema. The reason I bring this up is to prepare you for what I was not ready for. I did not know what little surprise we were going to get, and of course my goal here is to inform you. What typically happens as your baby's head is pushing down and coming out of the birth canal is that its head is also pushing down on your new mom's colon, and many times, my friend, the pressure will squeeze some poop out and onto the table. I don't even think Michelle knew that it happened, and of course, I didn't find it necessary to tell her. This is not a major deal, and the nurse will clean it right up. For the nurses, this is actually a good sign because it means that the baby is coming very soon.

The point here is that no one told me that was going to happen, so it was quite the surprise. Again, in the scheme of things to come, this is no big deal. However, I am telling you so you can be better prepared. It's a very common occurrence during the birth process, which brings us back to why some hospitals will offer your partner an enema. This being your first baby, everyone's kind of nervous and uptight, and what happens when we are nervous and uptight? We clench. Women clench because they are nervous about all of the pain they have been warned about. Her muscles will be tight, and when your body is in that kind of condition, it holds everything in. An enema helps to get everything out, if you know what I mean.

If she opts to get an enema, it's no big deal. They will bring her to the restroom. They will use a tube to flush her colon with water, she will go to the bathroom, and it's all good. Like most things, it's only a big deal if you make it one. At this point, she will either opt for the enema or not; then, once she's lying in bed, they will put the monitors back on and you guys will be hanging out and waiting.

This is a good time to talk about whether you are trying to go natural so we can cover all the bases. If she does want to try to go natural, a doula is a totally helpful and wonderful way to help facilitate that. I'll tell you why. Michelle decided she wanted to go for a natural birth, meaning no drug intervention, i.e., epidural. We did not have a doula present during our first birth, and we did in our second, third, and fourth births. Our first birth was the only one that had any issues.

A doula is a labor and delivery coach. Some doulas have nursing backgrounds, although some do not. However, all doulas are trained in labor-pain management and have a lot more experience supporting a lady giving birth than you or me. Doulas deliver hundreds if not thousands of babies, and there is a lot of evidence that shows that when a doula is involved in a birth, the possibility of problems happening goes down.[3] Why? For many reasons. One main reason is because she is a person on your team who knows what's going on and has the tools and know-how to help your lady and you to calm down. Doulas have relaxation tools and techniques they use to keep ladies feeling relaxed. Do you think you will really remember the details of what is going on during the birth process and what phase of movement the baby is in each step of the way? As good as you are—and you are good, my friend—a doula is a professional, and she's running her fingers through your lady's hair and telling her everything is going to be okay and knows it.

I remember when we were in the delivery room with our first baby, Eliana. I was telling Michelle, "Everything is great, honey, you're doing great!" And like in a movie, she looked at me and said, "How do you

3 Kenneth J. Gruber, Susan H. Cupito, and Christina F. Dobson, "Impact of Doulas on Healthy Birth Outcomes," National Center for Biotechnology Information Database (PMC ID: PMC3647727; accessed May 19, 2016), http://www.ncbi.nlm.nih.gov/pmc/articles/PMC3647727/.

know everything is okay?!" The truth is I didn't know, but you know who did? Penny, our doula. I am not getting kickbacks from any doulas, and yet I feel compelled to express how helpful Penny was through the birth process. She added to our experience by helping Michelle through the difficult times, all while keeping me involved in the process. Think about this: Because Penny was able to help keep Michelle more relaxed and calm, I was able to stay more relaxed and calm, which made the birth experience better for everyone. With Penny's help, Michelle was able to deliver our second, third, and fourth babies totally naturally with no epidural, and our smallest one was our son at eight and a half pounds—these were big-mambo babies.

If your partner plans on having a vaginal birth without an epidural or drugs, no matter who your delivering practitioner is, a doula is a fantastic idea that will increase her odds of success and is worth the extra money. Here is the disclaimer on having a doula. Doulas are typically involved with a birth when a woman wants to have her baby naturally. They take that seriously. Date a couple of doulas and make sure her and your views are in alignment, meaning if your lady wants to go natural, but then decides in the seventeenth hour that she just can't take it anymore and wants an epidural, that will be okay.

If your lady wants to go natural and you both have gone through the effort of having a doula, then she typically will go through with the process. After seeing Michelle do it three times naturally, I believe more women could if they had a doula to help. The point here is that if—and it is a small if—you and your partner find yourself in that situation and she wants the epidural, you won't have a conflict in the delivery room. The way to take care of that is to simply communicate what your wishes are and make sure that you and your doula are on the same page. Doulas are awesome ladies to have on your team.

Doulas are also an excellent resource, especially around the birth and delivery, if you need a night nurse or extra support after your baby is born. Doulas are usually part of a network of support people that you may need—pregnancy massage therapists, midwives, lactation consultants, and any other birth-related support persons you may need. Again, if she's planning on going natural, think doula! I highly recommend it! After we had Penny for our second birth, we called her before we even called our parents to let her know we were pregnant with our third and fourth so she could be ready. She added that much to our experience after what happened during our first baby's birth, which you will hear about soon.

If your partner wants to go natural and you are in a hospital setting and have an OB delivering your baby, you will be her main support person. Here are a few Hero Tools for you to use to help her while you are waiting for your baby. First, help her to have her change positions. Instead of her just lying in bed, have her walk around, or recommend that she goes on her hands and knees. Having her sit on the toilet or on an exercise ball you can bring will be a comforting position for her. You should also be conscious of her approach to working through contractions. If she is roaring and fighting through them, then coach her as a warrior: "Awesome job! Keep fighting!" Match her "tone," so to speak. If she is roaring and you approach her all calm like "Good job, honey, just keep breathing," she may punch you in the face! If she is working on being all Zen and breathing through her contractions, then approach her with more calm affirmations that will match how she is working through her contractions.

If your lady is planning on getting an epidural, that's 100 percent cool and her choice. In that case, you would not need a doula, although you could. Extra support is always a good idea! With an epidural, the key to remember is the time frame. There is a certain time she can get an epidural, which is typically after she is three to four centimeters dilated, although some women get it sooner than that, depending on her doctor. It may be considered too late at around nine or ten centimeters; if she is already that dilated, then the contractions will be coming very fast, and it might be difficult to get the needle in safely. If you want to be helpful, just communicate with the nurse up front that your team is opting for an epidural and to please let you know exactly when she is dilated enough to have one.

A couple of things to know about the epidural. To use epidural when delivering, your anesthesiologist will need to stick a very large needle — that's just what it is — through the disk space in your wife's spine.

The injection goes into the epidural space, which is one of the layers around the spinal cord. The word itself explains the process. "Epi" means *above*, because the injection goes above the "dural," meaning the dural layer that surrounds the spinal cord and coats it

NEEDLE
GOES
HERE

with fluid. From there, the epidural numbs the lower extremities. Approximately 61 percent of women in the United States of America have epidurals, and there are usually no problems after.[4] However, there are risks with any procedure: increased risk of instrumental delivery (forceps or vacuum), fetal malposition, a longer second stage of labor, fetal distress (compared with women who receive opiates intravenously or by injection), severe headache, maternal hypotension, maternal fever, and urinary retention.

4 Michelle J. K. Osterman and Joyce A. Martin, "Epidural and Spinal Anesthesia Use During Labor: 27-state Reporting Area, 2008," National Vital Statistics Reports 59, no. 5 (Hyattsville, Maryland: National Center for Health Statistics, 2011). Available online at http://www.cdc.gov/nchs/data/nvsr/nvsr59/nvsr59_05.pdf.

Just so you can get the other side of the road's opinion, my wife, Michelle, has experienced births both with and without an epidural. Michelle said that it was a night-and-day difference for the better when she did not have an epidural. Only our first experience was with the epidural. When it came time to push, she was numb, and she wasn't able to push as hard as she could without the epidural, which she would not have known if she had not gone without one during our subsequent deliveries. Just something to think about.

Michelle's second, third, and forth natural deliveries were much different than her first. After the baby was born, she was totally with it. She was able to walk and she wasn't numb, and her experience overall was just a better one. She was completely able to do it, and of course, it didn't hurt me at all. Going natural gets a lot of negative press, but she said it was worth it to go natural. So, if your wife is on the fence, you can let her know some positive feedback. At the end of the day, avoiding an epidural involves one less invasive procedure, which is one less chance of any negative side effects. Ultimately, I recommend thinking about all of your options and supporting your lady's decision, because she is the one doing the work!

Now that we have covered the different options for vaginal birth in a hospital setting, we will go over what to expect when you are going in for a scheduled C-section. If you have a C-section scheduled, start by showing up for your appointment. They will bring you into an operating room. You'll put on some scrubs, your wife will be gowned, and they will lay her down on the table with her arms out to her sides like a T. There is a curtain above her abdomen, and you're behind the curtain with her.

Some things to talk about before you get in the room: first, what do you want to do after the baby is born? Do you want to stay with your spouse, or are you going to go with the baby to the recovery room? Remember, my friend, that whatever she decides she wants you to do, her decision might change, so be prepared for that. You guys may talk about it and decide, yes, she absolutely wants you to stay with her. But when the time comes, she might change her mind and say, "No, no, no, I want you to go with the baby." Or she might say that she wants you to be with the baby, then at the last minute decide she wants you to stay while they sew her up. Just something to think about; remember to be flexible if it comes up.

In an emergency C-section procedure, that would simply mean that you're going in for a vaginal birth, either natural or with an epidural (either way, you're in the delivery room), and there are complications, and they tell you they need to do an emergency C-section. If that happens, then things are going to happen a bit more quickly. You will be either moved to a surgical suite, or the delivery room will be transformed into a surgical suite, depending on the emergency situation. If everything has been normal up to the point of delivery, you will usually have some notice that your lady may need an emergency C-section. Sometimes it is a right-now emergency, but other times your OB or midwife may not be happy with the baby's heart rate or another indicator of a potential problem that could give cause to get your baby out right away. If this is the case, they will let you know that they do not like how the baby's heart rate is looking and that if it continues, they may have to take the baby out.

ANYTHING CAN HAPPEN IN THE DELIVERY ROOM.

Remember, birth is a natural process, and you're not quite sure what's going to happen. My Hero Tool for you here is to be prepared for almost anything. You want to be able to make the best possible decisions, to support and help calm your wife down no matter what experience you have. It might be wise to talk about what your partner would want you to do in the case of an emergency C-section. Would she want you to stay with her or go with the baby afterward? God willing, everything is normal and healthy, but you just don't know when you go into that delivery room, which is a little scary—just like parenthood in general!

So, you're in the operating room and you're behind the curtain. You absolutely can look behind the curtain if you like. I've heard several different opinions for it and against it. More than one man has shared with me that they looked over the curtain and saw that the doctors had taken their partner's guts out to get the baby. It was quite freaky, and they would have preferred if they had missed that image. Some guys are totally cool with it.

There is a new trend starting in which moms are actually asking to have a clear curtain up during her C-section in order to watch her baby being born to feel more of a connection and to make the experience feel more like a natural, vaginal birth. This is new, and worth bringing up to your lady to see if that is something she may be into, and also worth asking your OB performing the C-section if she is willing to do it.

Regardless of whether you look, you will smell burning because they will be cauterizing as they cut through her abdominal muscles to minimize blood loss. When they get down to the uterus, they will cut it and they'll take your baby out. Just like in a vaginal birth, they will do the Apgar score and then the baby will go to the recovery room or the nursery, depending on what you choose while they sew up your wife, which could take up to an hour. You may have heard of the Apgar score before. It is an indication of how your baby made it through the birth process, checked one and five minutes after birth, and how she is doing outside the womb.

Apgar is an acronym:

Each category is rated from zero (lowest) to two (highest), with a total combined score of up to ten. A score of seven, eight, or nine means your baby is in a good range. Babies do not often get perfect tens. Again, this test is done right after birth and then at the five-minute mark to check on the general health of your baby, make sure they are breathing normally, and make sure they do not need emergency care.

One other helpful tool for you if your wife is going in for a C-section is to pay close attention while you're in the operating room to your significant other's non-

APGAR SIGN	2	1	0
APPEARANCE (SKIN COLOR)	NORMAL COLOR ALL OVER (HANDS AND FEET ARE PINK)	NORMAL COLOR (BUT HANDS AND FEET ARE BLUISH)	BLUISH-GRAY OR PALE ALL OVER
PULSE (HEART RATE)	NORMAL (ABOVE 100 BEATS PER MINUTE)	BELOW 100 BEATS PER MINUTE	ABSENT (NO PULSE)
GRIMACE (REFLEX IRRITABILITY)	PULLS AWAY, SNEEZES, COUGHS, OR CRIES WITH STIMULATION	FACIAL MOVEMENT ONLY (GRIMACE) WITH STIMULATION	ABSENT (NO RESPONSE TO STIMULATION)
ACTIVITY (MUSCLE TONE)	ACTIVE, SPONTANEOUS MOVEMENT	ARMS AND LEGS FLEXED WITH LITTLE MOVEMENT	NO MOVEMENT, "FLOPPY" TONE
RESPIRATION (BREATHING RATE & EFFORT)	NORMAL RATE AND EFFORT, GOOD CRY	SLOW OR IRREGULAR BREATHING, WEAK CRY	ABSENT (NO BREATHING)

verbal facial expressions or nonverbal communication, and this is why. Not long ago, I had an amazing new dad come to the class. He told a story about when they were in the operating room for his wife's C-section. He noticed that his spouse was making some expressions that were not necessarily happy. She was in pain; her face made it clear that she was uncomfortable. The typical sensation that a woman will feel when the surgeons are doing a C-section is described as having a tooth pulled: numb, although you feel the pressure of that yanking and pulling. His wife was feeling more than pressure. She was really in pain. That dad spoke up, and it turns out the medication was not doing its job. That superhero of a husband was on the job and took care of business. They fixed the medication and everything went smoothly after that, thanks to a hero like him who was paying attention and spoke up. This example goes to show that even in a planned C-section, anything can happen. So, there it is—you thought you were off the hook because she was not having a vaginal birth! However, you do have a job, and that is to pay close attention to her face while she is lying on that table, because you might have to speak up if something is wrong. If the dad who shared his story had been in Lala Land, he could not have swooped in and been a hero, and who knows what else could have happened.

After a C-section, you can expect a slightly longer recovery time. Some women will recover rather quickly after a C-section, and some will take more time. When you think about recovery time, think about what kind of shape your lady is in before the baby. It's not an exact science, but if she is in nice physical shape, does exercises, and has strong abdominal muscles, all of that comes into play when you're talking about recov-

ery from a surgical procedure. It will also mean that you're going to be on the dime a little more to help out, get the baby and bring her over, and do more of the schlepping work, at least until she's fully healed, which on average takes six weeks.[5]

You are now ready to support your lady through a C-section if you have one planned, and if you don't, you are ready just in case.

---

[5] Stephanie Watson, "C-Section: Tips for a Fast Recovery," Healthline, June 10, 2015, http://www.healthline.com/health/pregnancy/c-section-tips-for-fast-recovery.

Let's get back to the delivery room and get you prepared for what will go down with a hospital vaginal birth. You're in the delivery room. The monitors are on and you are basically just waiting around. Depending on the hospital or birthing center, you will probably be in a room with a DVD player and a radio, and depending on how comfortable your lady is, you could potentially watch a movie. When we went in for our first baby we brought VHS tapes—that is how far technology has come in thirteen short years! Bring a few movies you both like, or since she is the one pushing the baby out, maybe the movies can be "lady's choice." You can listen to music; maybe you are doing hypnobirthing and you plan on listening to some soothing meditations.

Here is another topic to bring up: "Honey, what are you open to during the time we are waiting?" Much also depends on what your birth plan is and if you have one. Typically, a birth plan is if your lady intends to go naturally; otherwise, there is not much need for one. If you do have a birth plan, the hospitals you're delivering in will typically be very experienced with supporting you and your plan. The nurses are usually fantastic, and if you just let them know what you're looking for, they'll help you. By that I mean that if you tell the nurses you are going to make an effort to do a natural birth and are not planning on getting an epidural, then they will not keep asking unless you change your mind. However, many women today opt for the epidural, and it is more commonplace; the nurses tend to assume you are getting an epidural, and that is why communication is key. It will put you all on the same page.

Absolutely post your plan up on the door with a piece of tape. However, between you and me, everyone is very busy around the hospital, and if it's a long novel, how many people do you think are going to stop and read a whole book? It's a lot easier just to express what you want; however, having it in writing is also nice. There's no right or wrong—please just don't post a plan on the door and expect that everyone knows what you want.

Consider speaking up and communicating to the nurses and everyone involved to know what your plan is. It's good enough that your lady is buck naked with her crotch out for everybody to examine—she's kind of in a compromised position, so she shouldn't have to be the one to express what your team wants from your birth experience. Things may change; however, you will cross that bridge when you get there. Initially, though, speak up.

Whether your partner is planning on having a vaginal birth, getting an epidural, or even delivering at home with a midwife, she will typically have an IV port put into her arm in case of an emergency. In the hospital, they will also take some blood because it will be needed if she does decide that she wants an epidural at some point. It's not like in the movies where she wants the drugs and the doctor appears and you have an epidural. When you decide you want an epidural, the anesthesiologist needs to order it up from the pharmacy. They mix up a batch specifically for your lady so it's exactly perfect; that's why they need to take some blood in the beginning when she is not in full-blown labor. After she requests the epidural, they'll need to call the anesthesiologist, which could take a little while depending on how busy they are. You usually have to wait for the anesthesiologist to come. Depending on your specific situation, you and your doctor will determine which anesthetic your lady will get. If she is going to get an epidural, then he or she will turn your wife on her side, give her a small, local anesthetic to numb the injection site, then administer the epidural needle—which is that big old needle—so they can insert a small catheter into the epidural space, which will stay in place to keep the medication flowing. Your lady could also get a "spinal," which is an injection as well. However, no catheter is left in, which is what Michelle had during our first birth. Obviously, there's no walking around after she gets the shot. You know how sometimes you see the ladies in labor walking around, trying to get the baby to move? No more walking. There's also no more eating after she has an epidural.

Typically, the baby comes pretty soon after she receives pain medication, and because she will be in less pain, she will be able to relax and all of the muscles of her crotch and her pelvis will relax, which really needs to happen for the baby to be delivered. Once the muscles of her pelvic floor are relaxed, that's when the dilation of her cervix starts rolling, and that's when your baby will come.

Another way that the hospital can help to induce dilation is to slowly introduce Pitocin, which speeds up the dilation process. At this point, if she was dilated through Pitocin or they had administered an epidural, once her cervix is dilated, your baby will be with you shortly. Get ready!

If your lady is going totally naturally with no epidural or Pitocin drip, then the time it takes to get to ten centimeters dilated takes longer. That span of time is where a doula really shines, because she has a whole bag of pain-management tools to help your lady relax as much as possible through that time frame.

A very common question that first-time dads often ask at this point is, do I watch the baby coming out? It is a big deal to a lot of guys. I once heard an interview on NPR with a writer who had recently had a baby. He said watching his baby be delivered was like watching his favorite pub burn down.

I'll let that sink in for a second.

While it is humbling to watch Mother Nature at work, watching is ultimately a decision you will have to make on your own. I will share with you that I watched all of our babies coming out. I went down south, so to speak, instead of staying up north, and it never interfered with our intimacy, which does happen for some men.

Today, men's roles have changed significantly, and we are expected to be in the delivery room and

involved in each and every aspect of the process. While this if great for most, there are some of us men who have trouble viewing their partner sexually after seeing their baby be delivered. Because being intimate with each other is both enjoyable and crucial to our relationships, if you are not into seeing the baby be delivered and already have negative thoughts about it, speak up. Better to communicate and stay by her side than be freaked out when your baby is delivered.

Having a baby together can lead to an amazing closeness and a bond that can increase your enjoyment of a healthy sex life and intimacy, which is obviously the best outcome. A friend of mine had a problem being intimate with his wife after their first baby was born because he would keep "seeing the baby come out," and that was a turnoff, as you may imagine. They went on to have more children, so he did get over it. They communicated about it and got through it. My purpose is to make you aware, not freak you out. Know yourself and make the best decision for your family.

With that being said, I understand it is not every day you see your baby exit your lady's vagina. Her vagina will be different after the experience, as will your relationship with her. If our ladies would complain, feel less attracted to us, or not want to be intimate with us when we go through physical changes (i.e., our bellies, our hair loss, or whatever it may be), there would not be any children being made. When you have a baby, consider choosing to be all in and "husband up" and get over it.

LOVE YOUR LADY—YOUR WHOLE LADY, THE MOTHER OF YOUR CHILD—AND NOT JUST HER VAGINA, WHICH WILL WORK PERFECTLY WELL, BY THE WAY, NO MATTER HOW MANY CHILDREN SHE DELIVERS.

Will it be exactly like it was before birth? No, but then again, neither will you.

You should know that realistically, if you are going to be in the room, there's a high likelihood that you will see the baby come out. That is why if you for sure do not want to see the baby delivered, make sure you stay by your lady's side. Most of the time in a hospital setting, a nurse will have one of your lady's legs and you will be holding her other. She will be kind of sitting up on the bed, pushing, once it's really time for this baby to be pushed out. It's kind of crazy; however, I was into the whole process, and if you are as well, then absolutely watch the baby come out. This could be a once-in-a-lifetime experience. What if this baby is your only baby? Birthing happens so quickly, and it's really a wild experience to see your baby for the first time.

The first thing you see will be the crown of their head. As your baby is being pushed out, the skin on their heads gets pushed together, and it looks like brains almost! If there are no complications, after the head comes out, the shoulders roll out one at a time—and then, your baby pops out! That's why I say—and you will really get it if or when you see it—that if you have to deliver the baby yourself, you need to remember counterpressure, because after the shoulders roll out, your baby is popping out!

If everything is normal and healthy, you have the option of cutting the umbilical cord. Again, ultimately your choice, although I highly recommend cutting the cord. It's another potential once-in-a-lifetime opportunity, and it's a neat thing to do. You will see if you opt to cut the cord how amazingly tough it is. I thought it would be easy like a ribbon cutting—*bloop*. It certainly is not like a ribbon cutting! You will find that the umbilical cord is a thick, fibrous cord, and of course it needs to be so strong because it is delivering all the nutrients to your baby. If you opt to cut the cord, the person delivering your baby will clamp the cord for you in two places, so you will just need to clip between the clamps. You will not need to figure out where to cut; don't worry about that. If you have decided to prolong the time before the cord is cut, you would have made that known already.

You choose to either cut or not cut the cord, and when that is done, they give the baby a little wipe down and hand her to her patiently waiting mom to bond. This is a good point to make some calls, let people know that everything is cool. You will then have your opportunity to hold your new bundle of joy.

By now a few minutes have passed, and in all the excitement of the baby being born, we tend to forget that they are going to deliver the placenta next. The nurses will have your lady pick up her tush and put what looks like a medical, blue-colored tablecloth underneath. In the front, there is a plastic pouch that will catch the placenta when it comes out. Delivering the placenta is typically not difficult. The nurse will usually massage your lady's stomach, and she might need to give a little push, and then the placenta comes out.

If you're going to save your cord blood, this is when that will happen. If you do decide to save it, then you will get specific directions on what to do, and you should have already communicated to the nurses that you were planning on saving it. This should definitely be one of the things in your birth plan. If you are delivering in a hospital setting, birth center, or at home, then you can rest assured that whoever has delivered your baby knows what to do as long as they know they are supposed to do it.

After listening to the many perspectives and discussions of the hundreds and hundreds of men that have been through class, the consensus is that saving your baby's cord blood is essentially like buying insurance. It is one of those things that is better to have and not need than need and not have! More and more stories are coming every day on lives being saved from having the cord blood, so if you can afford it, it's good to have. The advances have been amazing—even in the past thirteen years that we have been discussing it in class.

I met a young man who was saved by a cord-blood donation. This guy had three different kinds of cancers. He developed a very rare cancer in his liver when he was about seven. He was treated with chemo and got a clean bill of health, but the cancer came back when he was a little bit older. He was treated again, and given the all clear, but unfortunately, he ended up getting leukemia from the second bout of chemo. His life was ultimately saved by a cord-blood donation.

I must admit, my views have changed. If we could go back, we would have saved our baby's cord blood, or at least donated it, which is an amazing option if you do not have the cash to lay out. Please don't quote me on how much it costs; however, most guys report that there is an upfront fee of approximately one to two thousand dollars, plus a yearly freezer upkeep fee. The other option is to donate your cord blood to a cord-blood bank in a university research center, which does not cost you anything. If, heaven forbid, your child needs stem cells for a health situation, you will not get your child's exact cord blood back because chances are it would have been used; however, you will get a match if there is one for you. There are a few universities that are involved, and the list changes, so I will leave that to you to look up. Just Google "free cord-blood banking," and you will be on your way with all the information you need.

That is the story on the cord blood. The majority of guys say that if it's not going to take food off your table and you really want to have your baby's cord blood, it's worth the investment. If laying out the cash will take food off the table—and listen, these babies are very expensive—there are always cord-blood banks at universities that can do it for free. Or you can always decide not to save it at all. This can be one of your first parental bonding decisions. Good luck, whatever you decide to do.

During the placenta delivery and after you get to meet the baby for the first time, they will check him and give him an Apgar score. They will then give him back to Mom. The first crew cleans out and then the second crew comes in. They will bring your baby over to the "fry" lamp to keep him warm as they clean him up a bit more, take the little baby footprints, and get him weighed in. The nurses will then put on the little baby LoJack that goes around his or her ankle and a matching set on your wrists. These bracelets will set off an unpleasant set of reactions if you go past the Do Not Pass perimeter that is clearly marked on the floor in the maternity ward. Please do not be that guy who crosses that line; it is not a pretty situation. The whole place goes into lock-down, SWAT comes through the windows, the elevators shut down, the whole bit. Be careful. The extent of the lock-down is crazy, as it should be to protect your little, precious baby. If there are no complications at this point, you will be waiting for your recovery room to go recover!

To illustrate that anything can happen, let me share with you how I learned that lesson. Going in, you should know that Michelle wanted to go natural. However, she decided that if the time came, she would go for the epidural. We did not have a doula—we didn't even know what a doula was. If we had known, we would've had her with us for the first birth. We got to the hospital and Michelle was not fully dilated yet, and her water was not broken, although Eliana was already a week late and the contractions were getting closer and closer. Once we were settled into the delivery room, they broke her water, and then it was just a matter of time. And it took some time, my friend! After making it through *Pride and Prejudice, The Cutting Edge,* and *Rocky II,* we were still waiting. A full eighteen hours after we showed up at the hospital, she was still not fully dilated. Plus, she was exhausted—really exhausted! She hadn't eaten a real meal and she was pooped. She opted for the epidural.

They gave her the epidural as described, and then her lower half started to get numb and everything relaxed. Her pelvis relaxed, her pelvic-floor muscles relaxed, and the baby started to come out. Then the baby's heart rate started to rise because she was not progressing out. Eliana's head was hitting Michelle's pubic bone. We would soon find out that she was huge, at nine pounds nine ounces, and Michelle was going to tear. The midwife decided it would be better if she had an episiotomy, so they called in the surgeon. Now we were going from kumbaya with the midwife to the surgical lights and a whole crew of nurses assisting with this procedure.

In case you do not know, an episiotomy is when they cut the vagina to make more space for the baby to get through. The current theory is that the best thing to do is to let women tear. When we were giving birth, it made sense to us that the best thing to do was an episiotomy because you can sew the muscles and tissue together more neatly and more accurately if there's a clean cut versus if the tissue is torn and jagged. However, that may be something for you to discuss with your doctor. Listen, if they need to take action, whether they do an episiotomy or if you guys decide to let her tear, it is something to talk about in case you find yourself in that situation. We opted for the episiotomy, and it was a fourth degree. There are only four degrees of episiotomies, four being the highest, so it was a big one. But Eliana was able to be delivered vaginally without the use of a vacuum or need for forceps, which are tools sometimes needed to get the baby out when there are complications.

After Michelle had the episiotomy and Eliana was delivered, she was bleeding. On top of all the pressure from the baby, gravity pulls the blood down, so she was bleeding a lot! Her legs were numb, she was cold because of the epidural, and now she was bleeding profusely when they gave her that episiotomy — so of course I'm thinking, *She's dead, right?* I went from what was supposed to be this crunchy experience with the midwife where I was going to catch the baby to thinking that my wife was dying on the table and I was now going to be this dad raising a baby on my own. Although that didn't happen, the experience we were expecting also did not happen. Anything can occur in that delivery room. You just have to go with it and do the best you can. After Eliana was born, everything was relatively normal and fine, except for the fact that it took them over an hour and a half to sew Michelle up, and I stayed with her the whole time. Everyone that was waiting was in real suspense because they were all wondering what was going on.

Our second birth was of our son, Jonah, and was quite different than our first experience. Michelle at that time owned and operated a residential construction company with her father. One day, Michelle and her dad were out walking lots and looking at houses. On their way home, Michelle said to her dad, "You know, we are passing by my midwife's office. Let's stop in and get checked to see if I'm dilated." It was just about due-date time in July; however, she had not been in any real pain. The night before she was having some Braxton-Hicks contractions, and I was so tired that I convinced her to take a bath and relax, which she did. Come to find out, when she went in and got checked by the midwife, she was six centimeters dilated! They told her that she needed to go to the hospital right away. She called me, I headed over, and of course I called Penny to let her know we were en route—it was happening.

When I arrived at the hospital, Michelle was signed in and we had to wait for a few minutes before we got our room. Michelle's water still hadn't broken, and she was probably about seven or eight centimeters dilated. The nurse broke her bag of water with the crochet hook–looking tool; however, nothing really came out—Jonah's head was plugging the cervix, which is common. At this point, Penny, our doula, entered the room carrying her exercise ball, one of those big balls that is really comfortable for a delivering mom to sit on and bounce. My in-laws came soon after. In our hospital, you are allowed up to three people with you, and Michelle was cool with her folks being in the room. I asked her if she was sure she was okay with her dad watching this whole procedure, and she was cool with it. If she was cool with it, then so was I.

My father-in-law did end up getting some amazing photos, which will not be on the website, by the way! We were glad to have them, though. In most hospitals, you are allowed to take still photos; however, video is prohibited due to insurance issues—nobody wants any lawsuits. It worked out that before my mother-in-law, Marsha, came to the hospital, she had stopped at Boston Market and bought us some food. Score! We were waiting for something to happen, all hanging out and catching up, when my father-in-law dropped a piece of food on the floor. For the most part, we're "five-second rule" type of people when at home; however, this was not our house—it was a hospital. It's supposed to be all super sterile and clean, but of course he didn't eat it. But we all laughed and joked about the five-second rule. A few minutes later, Penny recommended that Michelle get on her hands and knees to try a more comfortable position than sitting on the ball. Michelle got on her hands and knees up on the bed, and suddenly we heard a stream almost right there in our room—not a brook, but a stream with a waterfall! As Michelle got her to her hands and knees, Jonah's head shifted and unplugged her cervix and all Michelle's water was flowing, everywhere, including by my father-in-law's feet, right where he had dropped his food.

We all lost it. It was so funny that everyone was cracking up, with the exception of Michelle, who thought she had just peed on herself! It was really funny and a huge relief because, although this was our second rodeo, the first time did not exactly go as planned and tension was high.

Michelle was pretty nervous, however. She was set on having a vaginal birth without the epidural this time. After her water broke and then came out, she dilated all the way. I was right there supporting her, although Penny was *awesome*! She was running her fingers through Michelle's hair and soothing her through the painful contractions. Penny brought Michelle to the bathroom where she could sit on the toilet, which was very comfortable due to gravity. She used her fingers like candles, having Michelle focus and breathe to blow out the candles. She brought a level of calm and a knowledge of the process that I certainly did not have and created a safer environment for Michelle to deliver naturally.

And she did! The time between Michelle dilating completely and her delivering Jonah may have been an hour. She was a trooper and she never tore at all. Jonah was the smallest of all of our babies at eight pounds and seven ounces. The midwife delivered the baby, and Michelle was totally with it. Her legs were not numb and the experience was wild; she pushed through. She almost gave up there for couple of minutes, but with the help of us supporting her, plus Penny and her tools, Michelle was able to do it—she delivered Jonah and he was totally fine. She is quite a lady!

The room cleared out. There were no surgeons and no crazy bleeding; just peace and quiet. Then she delivered the placenta and we waited for our room. This time around, with Penny, was a great, great experience.

With our third baby, Sarah, Michelle also went natural. We had a wonderful weekend, and Michelle was a few days past her due date, so we decided to induce the delivery with the approval of our midwife. We had the kids at a friend's house, took a walk through a local park, had a nice lunch, and then we met Penny at the hospital. After getting to our delivery room, the nurse broke Michelle's water and gave her some Pitocin to speed up her dilation. She was going to deliver without an epidural; however, she didn't want to wait all day to dilate. The nurses gave Michelle Pitocin slowly, and she did dilate to ten centimeters after about five hours. Sarah's birth had no issues. Penny again helped Michelle through, and Sarah was born at a whopping nine pounds, thirteen ounces, and with a full head of dark hair. I swear she was ready for a burger deluxe when she came out!

Lila, our caboose, was nine pounds, eight ounces, and also pretty smooth. There were no complications and no pain on my part, although Michelle would attest that even though this was our fourth rodeo and everything went smoothly, she did experience some seriously painful contractions, and squeezing the baby out was not a walk in the park. We experienced a little miracle with Lila. When she was delivered, we found her umbilical cord was in a loose knot. The knot never tightened or caused any issues, although it certainly could have been different.

As you can see, there is a pattern of our birth experiences getting smoother with each one.

My wish for you is that you and your partner are blessed with a trouble-free, healthy birth and that it is the experience that you want, whatever that may be, whether it is a vaginal birth, C-section, water birth, or home birth.

The key tool for you to use through the birth process is to be prepared for anything.

TALK ABOUT THE DIFFERENT CIRCUMSTANCES THAT COULD HAPPEN SO YOU CAN BE AS PREPARED AS POSSIBLE, OR AT LEAST A LITTLE MORE PREPARED FOR WHAT'S ABOUT TO HAPPEN.

On the topic of choosing who delivers your baby, be open. After listening to midwife/OB panels at baby fairs, this topic has come up. Turns out many women who want to try the natural route or even try a home birth are met without support from their partners. Mostly because many of us men are not familiar with the real knowledge to feel one way or another, and we say no because we are scared that something bad can happen and it seems that it would be safer to deliver in a hospital setting. Totally understandable! The truth by the numbers about the safest methods and places to give birth may not be what you think.

We chose to use a midwife practice and to deliver in a hospital setting. The practice had OBs as well in case of an emergency, like we had, or in hindsight, thought we had. We went the midwife route because with Michelle going natural, we thought our midwife would be in the room with us more often and be more hands on, and she was. Like in the movies, OBs—who are really surgeons and are good at what they do—are more intervention based and can sometimes, not always but sometimes, be less warm and fuzzy and less hands on during your partner's labor in their approach because of their training. An OB will usually come in at the very end when your baby is ready to be delivered, which works great if that is what you want. I want you to have a better idea of the differences.

As I got involved with prenatal education and learned more about midwives, turns out that by the numbers, using a midwife practice and having a "natural vaginal birth" can actually be the safest method to deliver, for your partner and baby. Mostly because giving birth is after all a "natural process" that has been going on for quite a long time, and from the beginning it was always tended to by midwives.

Today, if you opt to use a midwife practice, you can expect more personal care, longer office visits (in a good way), and more of a personal connection. "Women cared for by midwives are less likely to need pain medication, have more freedom of movement, and are more likely to eat and drink in labor. Women cared for by midwives are less likely to have routine interventions of any kind, have fewer complications, and are less likely to have a cesarean. In addition, there are fewer babies born preterm, with low birth weight, or with birth-related injuries when midwives provide primary care to pregnant women."[6]

With all that being said, a midwife, like an OB in a hospital setting, could be delivering other babies the same time as yours and be in and out of your room. This is another reason why we liked having our doula

---

6 Judith A. Lothian, "Safe, Healthy Birth: What Every Pregnant Woman Needs to Know," Summer 2009, https://www.ncbi.nlm. nih.gov/pmc/articles/PMC2730905/.

in our following experiences; our doula was in with us the whole time, letting us know where we were in the process, helping us, helping to relax Michelle, and keeping things calm. These were added bonuses that we never considered before because we, unlike you now, didn't know what we didn't know.

If you were wondering about delivering your baby at home with a midwife, the numbers in a recent landmark study show it is actually very safe if your partner is in the low-risk pregnancy category and there is a very low rate of interventions without increased risk of any bad effects for your partner or your baby.[7]

To be considered in the "low-risk" category, your partner would be:

- Older than seventeen and younger than thirty-five
- Have no diabetes, high blood pressure, HIV+, cancer of any kind, kidney disease, or epilepsy
- Free from genetic conditions like Down syndrome or genetic kidney, heart, or lung problems

---

7 Geraldine Simkins, "New Studies Confirm Safety of Home Birth With Midwives in the U.S.," Midwives Alliance North America, January 30, 2014, http://mana.org/blog/home-birth-safety-outcomes.

These are most of the qualifiers, although there are more not mentioned here.

Most women fall into the safe category; approximately 6–8 percent of women are truly high risk.

Although seeming a bit "out of the box," because today it is, if your partner is indeed a low-risk pregnancy and wants to have a home birth, there is strong evidence that supports it is a good idea, and you can feel confident it is safe with a qualified midwife delivering your baby.

IF YOUR PARTNER WANTS TO HAVE A HOME BIRTH, DELIVER IN A BIRTHING CENTER, A HOSPITAL, IN A BIRTHING TUB, WANTS TO GO FOR A VAGINAL BIRTH NATURALLY OR WITH AN EPIDURAL, YOUR SUPPORT IS CRUCIAL FOR THE SUCCESS OF A HEALTHY, SAFE OUTCOME. PLEASE LOOK INTO EACH OPTION BEFORE YOU KNOCK DOWN ANY OF THEM.

God willing, whatever method is decided, everything is normal and healthy with your lady and your new bundle of joy! You make your calls, you move into the recovery room, which is named appropriately, because after that birth experience, you both need a little recovery time! The recovery rooms these days are very comfortable. For you now, Daddy, there's typically a couch or pullout couch or reclining chair. You will be given blankets and pillows and you will be all set that first night. You can actually get to sleep. Your wife, not so much. She will be constantly woken up to have her blood pressure taken and make sure she's okay. The nurses will give her some pain medications and some stool softeners to help go to the potty because everything is sore and swollen from this whole process. When you get to the room, you and your new family really just hang out. You're hanging out and getting to know your baby.

I definitely recommend changing the first diaper (by the way, you will be a diaper-changing master—we will go over in detail why diapers are awesome and how to change them in Chapter 4, and you can watch the how-to video at TheHeroDad.com). Worst-case scenario, the nurses will help, especially if you are in there making the effort and ask for some assistance! All you would have to do is say to any nurse, "Hon, would you mind helping me with my first diaper?"

and you will be in business. (Calling your nurse "hon" is optional.)

You will be hanging around the room, getting to know your baby, and entertaining your visitors. Enjoy them, because with your fourth baby, you will be lucky to get a phone call!

With your first baby, it is honestly pretty weird. You are so used to being around big humans and now, you have your little baby, this little human being, a little person, but it almost doesn't seem like a little person. It seems like a little alien. With the little fingers, and the little toes . . . it's wild. You will see.

BABY'S RANGE OF MOTION

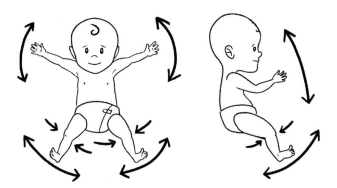

That's why you want to get in there and get over the weirdness. Move her arms and legs around to get a feel for your baby. Many men often express concern with knowing how much pressure or strength you can use; and how gentle you need to be while handling your baby. The single best tool that you can have to figure that out is getting in there and actually handling your baby. Move her arms and legs around, move her joints in their regular range of motion, her elbows, her fingers, and you will be able to figure out how to handle her by doing that.

If you choose to shy away from handling her right from the beginning, handling your baby will only get freakier the further you get. Parenting is on-the-job-training sort of work. Get in there. Change the first diaper or the first couple of diapers.

Your baby's first poop is called meconium. It is a thick, tarlike poop. His pipes are being cleaned out, so to speak, and it is kind of hard to clean off. It's all good, though—pooping is what you want your little dumpling to be doing. Totally normal, healthy stuff. You will get in there, change the first couple diapers, and you'll start getting familiar with your baby.

The next topic to think about if you delivered in a hospital and you are in your room is the nursery. Most nurseries probably operate the same way, although each may have its own unique differences depending on the size and location of your hospital. If your hospital has a nursery, you have some options for baby care during the nighttime, which is really nice! When night falls, everyone is going to be tired.

You'll have an option for your baby to sleep in the nursery overnight. You may have a fully staffed nursery with nurses in your home, which is fantastic. However, if there is not a staffed nursery in your home, you may want to consider using the hospital nursery during your stay. You will have no shortage of nights to be on your own handling and caring for your baby.

There are different options when it comes to using the hospital nursery. Your baby could sleep in the nursery all night long, which is nice—all you have to do is sign something that says it is okay for them to feed your baby formula. This presents one of the main issues or concerns when it comes to using the nursery overnight, which we will discuss shortly. The next nursery option is you can have your baby sleep overnight in the nursery, but they will bring your baby in to your partner to nurse when your baby is hungry, and then take her back to the nursery in order for you to get some sleep (great option if going to breastfeed).

The other option is, of course, for you to keep the baby in the room with you the whole time and figure out the whole feeding situation yourself.

You really will have time to figure out the feeding situation. Having the time and the opportunity to have a decent night's sleep may be a different story. Consider your options and talk about it with your lady. For our first baby, we decided to keep the baby with us our first night. In the middle of the night, we asked the nurses to take the baby and put her in the nursery.

There are a few issues that come up with giving the baby to the nursery overnight. The first is that your baby will get formula instead of breast milk. This could cause some concern if your lady is planning on breastfeeding. What you should be aware of is that breastfeeding is a supply-and-demand function of the human body. Of course, I thought when a baby is born, the mom's boobs fill up with a gallon of milk and she is good to go. Surprise! That's not how it works. The first milk that is produced is a very thick, nutrient-rich milk called colostrum, and there's not that much of it. Many times, your baby really might need to supplement a little bit in the beginning, especially if it's a big baby. My baby was over nine pounds, and she absolutely needed a little supplementation. Michelle was intending on breastfeeding, and she did with all of the babies.

Babies do not always need to supplement with formula; however, your baby may. Even though your spouse is excited and passionate about breastfeeding, try and reassure her that everything is cool and all is not lost if your baby gets a little formula the first couple of days. Michelle went on to breastfeed all four of our babies for at least six months, and they all had some formula the first couple of nights in the nursery and even some during the days until her milk came in.

The other possible concern about breastfeeding and overnight nursery stays is that your baby will have nipple confusion if he gets a bottle, meaning he will be confused when he gets Mom's real nipple, and it'll be an issue. Dad, most of the time it's only an issue if she makes it an issue. If you guys play it cool and your baby goes to the nursery and gets a little formula, and your lady is committed to breastfeeding and she has your baby latch on during the day and at night when he is hungry, there typically won't be any issues with your average, noncomplicated situation. You can rest assured knowing that your baby is being cared for in the nursery. You can get a good night's sleep, and then she can pick up the breastfeeding in the morning.

A bigger concern may turn out to be that breastfeeding in general is not as easy as it may seem, which is a heads-up for you to be supportive. Here is a tip from Michelle you might want to share with your lady if no one said this to her before. Breastfeeding is a bit of a process; Michelle found that if she can get through six weeks, everything clicks. It may happen sooner, but six weeks is a good goal for a woman to get started with. Michelle also was big on having a breastfeeding goal. Michelle's goal was six months.

She said that after six weeks it really got easier; the baby got the hang of it, and she got comfortable with breastfeeding. Some women, you snap your fingers and they totally got it, but others will have issues. One breast will not be producing as much, one nipple could be inverted—there is a whole industry around breastfeeding and classes and teachers and coaches. It's a big deal, and it's not as easy as you may think. I should say it is not as easy as *I* thought!

In regard to you using the nursery, ask around to some of your friends who have delivered at the hospital and ask them if they used the nursery. You'll find the consensus is that everything is cool if you're cool. My friend, seriously consider using the nursery. You will find that with a night's sleep, your new world will be a bit easier to handle. Your second night, your wife will not be woken up as much, and she will be able to sleep a little more, which will be very nice for her.

Although using the nursery is very nice and you can steal away some rest, please realize there is 100 percent nothing wrong with keeping your baby overnight. If you do, you're a real trooper! The rest of us will commend you. The nursery is yet another initial new-family decision you guys need to make, and you will make it when the time comes.

Let's talk about if you're having a son and you're going to have him circumcised in the hospital, as compared to having him circumcised eight days after the birth if you are Jewish. The main difference in the Jewish ceremony, which is called a bris, is that your baby will have some wine before he gets snipped (which he would probably appreciate), and of course the food after the event.

Circumcision in the hospital will typically take place the day after your son is born. What happens is

they will get your baby and bring him into a little surgical suite. He will be placed in a contoured foam pad
on a board, and he will be secured down with a strap
to prevent him from moving around. The same thing
would happen at home if you are having a bris. They
will use a tool that looks like a dental scraper, except
with a little ball at the end instead of a sharp point, to
break the adhesions between the tip of his little pecker
and his foreskin. Then they will pull the foreskin up
over his pecker and clamp it. Once that is done, they'll

take a blade and will slice off the foreskin. That's it. It is very quick, and after you see it you will realize why a little wine is a good idea.

Maybe a little wine for you if you decide to watch is also a good idea.

There's no right or wrong answer. Whether you both opt to circumcise your son comes down to personal preference. Once the doctor takes off the foreskin, they're going to dress his little pecker with some antibacterial cream, and then wrap some gauze around the tip. A pecker is very vascular, and the healing process is usually complete within two weeks. It should look totally normal within that two weeks. If it's not, you really need to bring him in to the doctor to have a look. However, after a normal procedure without any mishaps or issues, you're looking at about two weeks of taking care of his little pecker. We'll go into detail about doing that when we get into diaper changing in Chapter 4.

I do want to take a minute to bring up a valid concern that one of my new fathers-to-be had in a recent class. Let's call him Charlie. Charlie's baby boy was due in a few weeks. Charlie and his wife wanted to circumcise their new son, but he was nervous about the circumcision. He knew three families that had recently had their sons circumcised in three different hospitals, with three different doctors, and all three had issues with their son's little pecker after the circumcision.

Whoever did the procedures messed up, and the little boys were having issues with their pecker not healing way after the two-week mark. The doctors did not do a good job. He didn't share all of the details, but he did say that there were issues even a month after the procedures, which is definitely not normal.

Charlie was concerned, as you and I might be if you personally knew of three different goof-ups. Do you really want to explain to your son why you didn't do anything to make sure he had a good doctor working on him? This is what you can do. You do have power to take some action in this department. If you do decide that you want your son circumcised and you're in the hospital, find out who will be doing the circumcision if it's not one of the doctors from your OB practice that you know. Find that doctor—you should be able to have him or her paged—and have them come to your room so you and your wife can talk to them. If it is the OB from your practice or an OB from another practice on call at the hospital, you have every right to ask them what their track record is with the circumcisions that they have performed, any incidents they have had, and if they had any record of problems. You are totally in the right to ask about the physicians treating your baby. If you talk to this doctor and you don't get a good feeling from that person or their track record, request another physician.

As fate would have it, that day in class we had another dad-to-be who was from Canada, and he agreed that you should take advantage of the fact you can ask questions and even request another doctor if you feel it is necessary. With the health system in Canada, they don't really have a say in what doctor they get, or who's treating them, whereas in America we really do have the right to ask and choose because we are paying. Just like you picked your OB or your midwife, you can, if you choose, check out who is planning on snipping your boy. It's a right that can increase the odds that everything will be okay.

Surgeons do have high egos and can be easily offended. If you lead off with the story about Charlie and the poor circumcisions, and that you are just concerned about your new baby's safety, the odds are everything will be cool. However, if the surgeon gets bent out of shape because you asked about his track record, tough luck! Your main concern is your baby's safety, health, and his pecker—which I guarantee he would like to have working properly now and in the future!

Heaven willing, everything will run smoothly for you and your son if you do decide to have a circumcision. After the procedure, when all goes well, your little trooper will be tired and he will either come back to your room or to the nursery and get some rest.

All righty then, let's get back to your room, where you will be essentially hanging out. At some point, you're going to be filling out forms, such as your baby's birth certificate and social security papers. You can handle the paperwork to take that off your wife, unless your wife wants to do it. One thing for you to gain from our third hospital experience is to be absolutely certain about the name you write on the birth certificate. Our Sarah, who is now ten, was Simone for a night. We really liked the name Simone—it's beautiful—so we filled it out on her birth certificate. However, after getting to know her a little bit better and spending some time with her, we decided that Simone was more of a Sarah to us. But her birth certificate was already handed in. The nurses told me that they drop off all the birth certificates at the mail room. I tracked down the mail room and asked them for the certificate. They literally were about to throw that thing in the mail!

If you change your mind but you miss the certificate, you will be able to find it at your local department of live birth and death certificates, which is where you would pick up your baby's actual birth certificate in a month or two, by the way. It's a bit of a hassle going to pick up copies of the birth certificate, so I can't imagine going down to change it will be a pleasure cruise, not to mention an additional cost to get it done. So please, please, make sure that the name you want for your baby is the one that goes onto the certificate. Your hospital will typically mail them out every day.

You will also probably be visited by a lactation consultant, which is great if your partner is breast-feeding. If she has tried breastfeeding already, she can get some pointers and ask some questions before you guys leave. You will also be visited either the first day or second day by your pediatrician if you have picked one already, and your doc will come and check your baby and say hi. If you don't have a pediatrician, then the hospital will have one come in and check out your bundle of joy.

Hospitals sometimes also have photographers that come into the room and offer to take a picture of your new family. You can figure that stuff out if and when it happens.

Another situation to bring some attention to is while you guys are hanging out in the room and family and friends are coming to visit, it's exciting and also sometimes tiring. Try not to feel bad if you need to let your friends know that your partner or baby is tired and that it's time to go. The people who make the effort to be there are typically close friends and family, and odds are all will be cool; just be conscious of that random friend who doesn't get the point that it's time to go. You can always ask your nurse to let people know it's time to go, and you can also come up with a secret signal that your lady can give you if she feels like she is ready for a break from company.

So, you're hanging out and everything is cool. You are both getting to know your baby a little bit and getting more comfortable holding a bottle, changing the diapers, and swaddling. These are all tasks that will be covered in Chapter 4. You absolutely do not need to be worried about them. After you read the chapter on soothing your crying baby, you will be a champion diaper changer and swaddler.

Before you know it, it will be time to check out and head home. Inform your nurse on duty that you're ready to rock 'n roll, and then they'll work on the discharge papers. Next, while that's all happening, you will typically be given a cart to take all of your bags and baby gifts out to your car. Then you will drive your car around to the exit or baby-pickup area, which is designated just for drop-off and pickup. You can either have your baby's car seat up in your room already or bring it up now. (Your car seat is another topic we will cover in detail in Chapter 7, the safety chapter, just so you know.) After you plop Junior into the car seat, maybe you will take a couple cute pictures for her first ride home. Then your partner will be seated in a wheelchair, the nurses will put your baby on her lap, and she will be wheeled out with you to the car. The doors will open, and you will get your first breath of fresh air in your face as a family. You will then secure the car seat into your car base, help your lady into the car, and head home.

That ride home is like in the movies—kind of scary, maybe more surreal. Depending on whether you have somebody waiting at home to help you or if it's you two headed home for the first day on your own, it's a pretty amazing trip. You have so much going on at that time that you might miss one of the most amazing aspects. However, try to take a minute to think about how you two are literally new people in a good way. You and your partner walked in as a pregnant couple, and you're leaving as a family! Pretty awesome.

CHAPTER 3

THE TRANSITION HOME

YOU did it! You supported your partner through the birth of your child, you have yourself a new baby now, and you're headed home. So exciting! You might feel confident and ready to get rocking and rolling, but to those of you who are a little nervous, I hear you, brother! I remember when Michelle and I left the hospital with our first baby, Eliana, we didn't even go home. We were so scared of what it meant to be on our own and take care of our new baby with no nurses or nursery to help us—it was quite unsettling. So, what did we do? We went to Babies "R" Us, put Eliana in the cart, and roamed the aisles for what seemed like an eternity. They had to kick us out at closing time! At that point, we had to face the music, so we went home. After reading this chapter, you'll feel more prepared than Michelle and I did, and ready to settle in at home with your new addition to the family.

Here let's talk about the physical changes that are going to happen to your home when you introduce a baby into your habitat. In the next chapter, we will cover caring for your baby when you get home. Before we get into the meat and potatoes here, if you have animals at home, this book covers introducing your baby to your pets in the safety chapter (Chapter 7). Don't worry, we're absolutely going to cover pets, but for now, let's just talk about getting you home, getting settled in with the new baby, and how to make that transition as smooth as possible.

Let's now address the actual physical changes that you need to make to accommodate your baby. Up to this point, you and your significant other have created a comfortable home that you enjoy living in. However, you will need to make some tweaks to create a baby-friendly home, without a doubt. Many, many, many, many times men have expressed to me that their house is so upside down that they don't even recognize it anymore—and the baby hasn't even come home yet!

Just as it's important to discuss your dreams and visions of your new life and parenting plans with your partner in parenting, it's equally as important to touch on your vision of your home. Think about creating a world that you and your woman will continue to want to come home to. This includes both your emotional and physical environment.

To make for a comfortable transition, consider weaving what you like about your habitat as it is with your new needs. It's a huge deal to accommodate and introduce your new baby into your home, but does that have to mean a 100 percent change? Is your place really so dangerous that it needs a 180-degree baby makeover? Chances are, it doesn't. There is an excellent documentary that I recommend called *Babies*. The documentary follows four babies from infancy to one year, all raised in different environments around the world, from a posh apartment to a remote farm. It's amazing, but whether a kid has every luxury imaginable or sleeps in a drawer with a blanket, the documentary shows that each baby adapts to their environment. They all develop and function perfectly fine. The moral of the story is that your baby will adapt to your habitat. As long as it's safe, there's no need to change your home 100 percent.

If you are 100 percent okay with changing everything, that's cool. However, if you are hesitant, then listen to your gut and talk about it. The key is having the right mind-set. Remember that you both have been living in your home comfortably. When you decided to become parents, you decided to invite your new baby into your home to live with you. Children are sort of like extended houseguests. Now, don't take this the wrong way—children truly are a miracle. But let's face it: If things go well, your baby will grow up to be a productive, confident member of society and fly the coop when he or she turns eighteen. Would you invite a houseguest in and let them change everything about your home?

Think about the last baby party you went to with all the people who also have or are about to have a new baby. Think about the couples who seem genuinely happy and are really enjoying their experience with their new baby. Now think about the other people at the party, you know, the miserable ones who do nothing but complain about how much their world has changed, how it's nothing but work, and how they are not having a good time. If you took a poll of those people, how many of the complainers do you think would admit that their home habitat was changed close to 100 percent? You can bet that a high percentage of those people never speak up about what their needs or wants are to help maintain a balance.

They probably never heard that it's okay to speak up and say nicely, "Hey, hon, let's try to keep a bit of balance here as we incorporate our new baby into our world. We don't need to change our entire habitat to make the baby happy." Truly content parents are the ones who realize that their babies will be happy if they and their partner are happy. Remember, you want to take care of the home team who is running the show as well as your new addition. Taking on your new parental roles does not mean you can forget about your husband-and-wife roles.

If you want to increase your odds of being happy, you have to communicate about your vision, about your feelings, and about keeping some balance, because if you don't, your world could turn upside down, and you will risk the unhappy feelings of walking through

the doors of a home you do not recognize and may not be happy with.

Of course, there need to be some changes to your home. You want your baby to have a safe, fun, peaceful place to explore and grow. Just remember, you also need to have a safe, fun, peaceful place to come home to and live in, which will help to keep you in the genuinely happy group at your next party.

Let's talk about some other environmental factors that come up in almost every one of my classes. The first one is temperature. What temperature is the right temperature to keep the house when you bring your baby home? Again, the answer comes back to the fact that your baby will adapt. If you keep your home at a temperature that you and your wife are comfortable with, odds are your baby will adapt. However, keep in mind that the baby's sensory functions are still being developed. Somewhere in the middle is typically a good place until your baby can fully self-regulate their temperature, which is about six to ten months.

The other topic that we need to talk about while we are getting ready to bring the baby home is teamwork. Teamwork is one of the foundational principles of raising your baby and creating your home together. Your odds of success will depend greatly on you and your partner's ability to come together as a team.

We all have our different roles that we play in the home, and only you know which roles you will fill. As in any workplace, the same goes for the home— the more roles you can fill, the more valuable you will prove to be for the team.

You may be going back to work or be the stay-at-home parent, but whatever your situation, everyone has their roles and responsibilities. There is one job that a lot of men don't take on, but if you do, you will increase your value at home and with little effort. That job is laundry.

Laundry piles up fast. It's not a huge deal for two people, but when you have a baby, your laundry increases exponentially. If it's accepted in your home that you're not the laundry guy, that's cool. But if you want an easy way to move yourself into hero status, dabble in helping with the laundry. If a load of laundry needs to be thrown in the wash or switched to the dryer, just do it. Fold it, separate it, and put it away. It will go extremely far in helping the house run more smoothly.

Now for the laundry tool that will bring your laundry contribution to the next level. When you're switching laundry into the dryer, take out your lady's bras. That's right—do not dry the bras in the dryer. The dryer often will melt the bra clips. Sometimes you can get away with bending the clip back with pliers; however, save yourself the trouble and just put them on the doorknob or a hanger to air-dry. Bras can get expensive—nursing bras, jogging bras, regular everyday bras, sexy bras— each one adds up. Besides the cost, she has her favorite bras that she really likes to wear. Especially if she will be nursing, she will definitely have her favorite nursing bra that she would prefer not to have ruined.

The thing about laundry is that even though you may not have been called on to run laundry before, you probably know how to run a washing machine. If not, it is certainly easier than working a smartphone, and you can figure it out really easily. Laundry is a good way to help out, and you could start helping today.

So, there you have it. If you share your feelings about your changing habitat to help keep a bit of a balance and chip in when you can with the laundry, transitioning your home will become easier, and you can add two more tools to your bag that will go a long way to increase your happiness and the happiness of your spouse and your new addition.

CHAPTER 4

SOOTHING YOUR CRYING BABY

ALL right. You are home hanging out with your brand-new baby, you have defrosted dinner from the freezer, and you're ready to do some laundry. Now it's time to learn the different tasks you will need to care for and soothe your baby. These tasks are the nuts and bolts of parenting your infant, and with the accompanying tools, you will be prepared for the challenges ahead and emerge a hero.

Let's jump right in. You're on duty and you're willing and able to do your part when your baby starts crying. What's the first thing you do?

When it comes to the baby and all things new with the baby, the key is to stay calm. Anytime there's a situation with the baby, the outcome will always be dramatically improved if you stay calm, no matter what.

IF YOU KEEP A CALM HEAD ABOUT YOURSELF AND DON'T FREAK OUT, YOUR CHANCES OF DOING SOMETHING RIGHT AND FIXING THE PROBLEM WILL BE A LOT GREATER THAN IF YOU PANIC. IF YOU HELP YOUR PARTNER TO KEEP CALM AS WELL, THE SITUATION WILL ONLY BE IMPROVED. UNDERSTANDING AND USING THESE TOOLS WILL HELP YOU TO KEEP CALM.

First thing you want to do is take three to five breaths in through the nose and out through your nose.

Getting in the habit of consciously taking three to five breaths before you handle your baby will serve you now to get centered to manage your brand-new infant's needs as well as in years to come when you are explaining for the hundredth time not to flush toys down the toilet.

After you get centered, survey the scene. You have a crying baby that needs some attention. The first and easiest thing to check and fix is the diaper. Diapers are super easy to check; it takes two seconds, and if that's the problem, it is super easy to fix. As a parent and a dad, you will learn to love situations that are easy to fix. Experienced parents will do a sniff test, or simply look and feel for a heavy load that your baby is toting around.

A dirty or full diaper is usually not a secret, although sometimes they do make sneaky poops that you need to look in the diaper for. You have identified that your baby needs a diaper change. But first, before we get into the details of actually changing the diaper, let's talk about what sort of diapers to purchase for your baby.

I have a friend who's an engineer. He works in the business that creates the gel inside diapers that absorbs the moisture and other brown contents. I've heard straight from the horse's mouth that regardless of the brand, the materials used in mostly all disposable diapers and the gel inside them are essentially the same. Depending on what country you live in, there are some diapers with better or worse technology. However, in the United States, most diapers contain high-quality gel. My son, Jonah, even did an absorption test in school where he poured water into different brands— not one leaked.

When it comes to diapers, your tool is that it's less about the brand and more about the fit.

Some babies are tall, some are short, some are chunkaroos, and different diapers have different elastic waistbands and leg elastic. However, a fancier design does not necessarily mean it will be the best fit for your baby. Look around their thighs for a nice, tight fit. You want to be able to get a finger or two inside any area where there is elastic in contact with your baby to make sure it is not *too* tight. The same goes for the waistband. You want to secure the diaper nice and tight while still being able to fit one or two fingers inside the waistband. Choosing diapers with a proper fit over design or brand will surely save you money.

If you're looking for more ways to save on diapers, here's a Hero Tool that one of my dads shared with our class. When his wife had a baby shower, he invited his buddies over to play a game of poker. The ante was a box of diapers.

He divided out who would bring what size by their names. A through K brought infant diapers, L through S brought the next size, and so on. This is a smart and fun way that you can get a ton of diapers in different sizes, which is one of the items you need most when you have a new baby.

Michelle and I have gone across the diaper spectrum with our four kids, from big-box, store-brand diapers to name-brand diapers, and as long as they fit well, we have been happy with the functionality of all of them. Wipes, on the other hand, are a different story. Not all wipes are created equal, and some of them, frankly, suck.

Not mentioning any names, but if you go with the really inexpensive wipes, you are upping your odds that they will rip as you pull them out of the package and will be unusable if you even get them out. What a waste of money! You want to find some good wipes because if you are out and about and changing your baby, the last thing you want is for your finger to break through and get a finger full of poop, right? That's why wipes are key. The best wipes that I have found were Kirkland wipes. If you have a Costco around you or you have access to Kirkland wipes, I've found that those are very strong, cost effective, and have never failed me. I happen to like those, but there are a lot of other good brands. Find one that you like and that does the job.

Some parents also use a wipe warmer, which is a little box that you plug in to keep the wipes nice and warm. A word of caution: babies are a recording device. From the minute you bring them home, they are listening to and watching you, and you're training them on what to expect from you. So, while the wipe warmer is nice, pay attention to what you're getting your kid used to. Let's say that every day they're getting treated to nice, warm wipes. It's a royal treatment—imagine you wiping your behind with nice, warm wipes every day. That sounds good, right? I would like it also, and the kids grow to love it!

However, let's say you're at your buddy's house watching the game with the baby, and they don't have a wipe warmer. Your baby might get pissed off that there're no warm wipes. After all, that's what he is used to. There is no right or wrong answer to using a wipe warmer; I'm just bringing it up as something for you to think about.

Another tool you will need for changing diapers is a travel mat. The reason you need a travel mat is that the safest place to change a baby is on the floor. The changing table is great, but you have to be very careful because you never know when the baby will decide to roll over and possibly off the table. For convenience, try to find a travel mat with a little compartment for wipes and extra diapers like the Hero Dad changing pad. You'll want to have yours with you at all times.

If you do use a changing table, remember to lean against the table, acting as a wall, and always keep one hand on the baby. Brand-new babies don't roll much; that happens in a month or two when they start moving around more. However, be conscious and especially careful on a changing table, because you never know when they will start moving, and they might roll on you when you least expect it. I know that, by the way, because it happened to me when I was changing my son, Jonah. I was just reaching, reaching, reaching for something, and *bloop*—he fell on the floor. PS, I didn't tell my wife for three days about that! Luckily, everything was okay.

Take your baby to wherever you are going to change her—the changing table, a mat on the floor, or wherever you feel most comfortable—and let's get into actually changing the diaper.

IF YOU NEED HELP VISUALIZING, YOU CAN ALSO VIEW THE VIDEO ON THE HERO DAD METHOD OF CHANGING DIAPERS ON MY WEBSITE, WWW.THEHERODAD.COM.

The diaper-changing method I'm going to explain to you is not your typical changing method. You might have heard of an issue that some babies have called colic—this method could help to prevent it. A baby with colic can be a real struggle. Doctors have yet to discover what causes colic, though it is believed to be gas pains and/or gastric or intestinal discomfort, which makes them quite fussy and sometimes inconsolable for hours on end. As part of the health-and-wellness world, I have learned one theory on colic you might not have been privy to.

Whether you're a baby or an adult, the nerves that control the intestines in all human beings originate from your lower back around your lumbar spine. These nerves are the power lines that control your large intestine, small intestine, and your digestion processes. Constantly lifting your baby's legs up to his head repeatedly every day several times a day could irritate their lower back, as your lower back could potentially be irritated if someone were to take your feet rapidly to your head and hold them there more than several times a day. That repetitive motion could irritate the lower back and could in turn irritate the power cables supporting digestion, which could cause or at least increase the risk of colic. The method I recommend you use avoids bringing his feet up to his head and cranking up his lower back altogether. The Hero Dad method of changing your baby is done by rolling him on his side. It is super easy and better for their little spine and makes it much easier to clean them.

This is how it works: whether a boy or a girl, the first thing you are going to do after laying your baby down is to gather your supplies—a clean diaper, wipes, and a garbage can close by. Undo the two sticky flaps of the diaper. Then take the front flap of the diaper and use it to wipe down his or her little pecker or vagina. Whether it is a pee or poop, the process is the same.

Next, push that front flap flat between their legs and then gently roll your baby on their side toward you. Now their whole tush and back are totally exposed without bringing their legs up over their belly. This method is also better because when you bring their

CHANGING A DIAPER

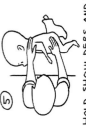

① PLACE BABY ON CLEAN SURFACE

② PEEL BACK SIDESTRIPS

③ UNFOLD FRONT, USING FLAP FOR INITIAL WIPE

④ WIPE BABY'S FRONT

⑤ HOLD SHOULDERS AND HIPS AND ROLL TOWARDS YOU

⑥ IF ON CHANGING TABLE, STAND WITH BODY AGAINST EDGE AS A WALL

⑦ PULL DIAPER OUT AND TO THE SIDE

⑧ WIPE BOTTOM

⑨ ROLL ONTO BACK

⑩ WIPE FRONT COMPLETELY —ALL NOOKS AND CRANNIES. FOR GIRLS, ALWAYS WIPE FRONT TO BACK

⑪ ROLL BACK ONTO SIDE

⑫ HOLD DIAPER AGAINST BOTTOM

⑬ ROLL ONTO BACK

⑭ HOLD FRONT FLAP IN PLACE WITH HAND

⑮ ATTACH SIDE STRIPS. DONE!

feet up to their belly, you can't really see underneath, where you are supposed to be cleaning.

As they are on their side, pull the dirty diaper out and put it off to the side close by, but not close enough for the baby to smack their hand in it. Use your wipes to clean up their back and tush. You can put the dirty wipes into the old, stinky diaper if it wasn't a total explosion. Once their back and tush are nice and clean, turn them on their back and make sure their front is totally clean. If you have a chubby chunkaroo, they could have gotten poop in the little folds of their thighs, so make sure that's clean too.

With girls, you really need to wipe them from front to back because you want to avoid any poop getting in her vagina. This could cause a yeast infection, and we don't need any extra issues going on down there. In reality, though, when they poop, you are going to accidentally wipe from back to front sometimes; it just happens. The key with girls is to double-check before you finish and put on a fresh diaper to make sure her vagina is clean. Open it up, wipe down from front to back, and make sure that it is clean.

Now fold up and seal the old, stinky diaper with the sticky flaps and toss it. Roll your baby back on their side, take the fresh diaper, and as you put it on their back and tush, spread your fingers out across the band at the top of the diaper. You will probably be able to reach across their whole back with your hand, which will hold the diaper in place. Pull the front flap through their legs and then lay them on their back. They should be lying on the clean diaper with the front flap through their legs, ready to be secured in the front.

Grab the front of the diaper, pull it up and over their little privates, and spread out the front band over their belly with your hand. Then grab the sticky flaps on each side and secure them in place. Adjust the straps nice and snug. You do not want the straps to fall off, but you also want to be able to fit two fingers in the band when all is said and done. And that is it! You, my friend, are now poised to be a diaper-changing Hero Dad!

Well, almost. There's one last item that we need to talk about before we move on from changing the diaper, and that is your garbage can. It's important to think about how you're going to get rid of the dirty diapers once your baby is all clean and wrapped up. The Genie is very popular and has been around a long time. It really does a nice job; however, the Genie needs its own special bags, which they don't sell in typical stores. They are usually sold in baby stores, which means that you need to make a special trip to the store for those bags, and that's a bit of a pain in the tush, especially because you know what a special trip to the baby store means—it means coming home with more "stuff" that you probably do not need! Then there is the Champ, which is a good choice. It does its job, and you can use regular bags in the Champ. However, just like the Genie, you are storing up the poop in the room inside that giant bucket. I don't care how many layers of plastic there are on there—a big bucket of poop is still stinky and full of bacteria.

There is one other option that a lot of people don't really think about that saves you dough and helps the environment: reusing. Ahhh, reusing. What kind of bags do you typically have and get on a consistent basis that you could reuse? Bingo! Grocery bags! You can buy one of those small garbage cans with a lid that fits on a desk. You could have a bunch of grocery bags stored up right behind it or in a little box, or you could stuff a bunch of them into one bag and keep it in the room. If you get a couple pees, they're okay to sit in that little garbage can. Once you get a poop, tie up the grocery bag, bring it down, and throw it away with the regular garbage. That way, you save a couple bucks on bags and save the environment, too.

Now, what about lotions and creams? Should you use that stuff or not? The truth is you and your woman will typically do whatever your family tradition dictates. For example, if your mom always used a certain lotion on you, that is what usually happens unless you and your partner decide to start a new tradition.

You should know, though, that the creams and lotions serve as a moisture barrier, and that's a good thing. Remember that your baby's skin is very sensitive, so if they are sitting in pee or poop for little while, even if you are doing a good job changing them, their skin gets irritated quickly! Oftentimes, creams and lotions are a good thing to keep the baby dry until you get to change him.

Another important skill is caring for your son's little pecker if you had him snipped. After the circumcision, you're going to get instructions on how to maintain his pecker from the doctor or mohel. But just to get you ahead of the curve, here is how to address a healing circumcision. It is really easy.

You need to change the dressing or bandage every time you change his diaper. You won't have to do this forever, because it should be healed completely in about ten to twelve days. All you have to do is put on a little antibiotic ointment like Neosporin and then wrap it with gauze. His pecker should be looking pretty normal in seven days or so. If it's not, then that is cause to bring him to the pediatrician.

While we are talking about boys, here is another tool for you: always make sure you point their pecker down in the diaper. Otherwise, there is a good chance they can pee up and out of their diaper and into their outfit, especially if their diaper is too loose. That combo will almost certainly deliver you some wet, pee-smelling outfits, and who needs that extra work?

Another thing to be conscious of when you're first starting to change your baby is that when air hits their privates, they will shoot a little stream of pee—even girls will shoot a stream of pee from time to time. Be careful with boys because they will shoot straight up, as they are little aiming devices. You *will* get peed on; try thinking of it as a rite of passage. It happens to the best of us. Just try and avoid being open mouthed and smiling at your bundle of joy for the first week or so, or you will increase your odds of getting it right in the mouth!

You can, of course, purchase a peepee teepee, or you can just use a washcloth to cover his little pecker and save the money!

Now, a couple of thoughts for you on diapers in general, and then a tool that will seriously set you apart from the crowd as a Hero Dad.

Some guys are excited and not worried at all about the whole diaper business. Others are really fearful about changing diapers. It's totally normal if you are a bit nervous; after all, it's a task you might have never done before. I'm here to tell you that diapers are awesome.

YOU SHOULD CONSIDER EMBRACING DIAPERS AND DIAPER CHANGING, AND THIS IS WHY: CHANGING A DIAPER USUALLY LENDS ITSELF TO SOME QUIET TIME AND BONDING WITH YOUR BABY.

You usually go to another room or someplace else where it is a little quieter and out of the crowd. It's a nice, quiet time that your baby is lying there unhappy, and you can make him happy relatively easily. Not to mention, it can be a break for Mom. A win-win-win: You get to bond, your baby gets a nice, clean behind, and your wife gets a break!

Look, can it sometimes be disgusting? Of course. But we are not the babies here. You just had a baby— you are a man now. If you have ever helped a friend who got a little too drunk and had to clean them up after a great night that they surely didn't remember, then you have dealt with yucky before. And now this is your yucky, so you need to get over it!

In case you are still not sold on the idea that changing diapers is a good time, let me help your perspective by taking you on a little journey. Close your eyes and come with me down the road just a little bit, about three years. You have been doing amazing. You and your wife still like each other, and you are becoming a confident, involved dad! Both of you are especially excited because you will be potty training your kid! Very exciting times! Well, when you get through it, just think—there are no more diapers, more money in your pocket, traveling is easier, and of course they look soooo cute in their big-kid undies and panties!

So, one day your big boy or girl, who has been doing awesome and has not had an accident in a while, is on a trip with Daddy to the store. Things couldn't be better. Then what's going to happen is that your big kid is going to take a big-kid poop in his big-kid undies. It is going to be truly disgusting, and I hope for your sake it's not diarrhea.

You will not have your diaper bag or wipes or any tools because you just ran out for one thing and they were doing really well. You, my friend, are going to have to punt. You're going to get it worked out, of course, but it will be an experience to remember.

Flashback to the present. What was my point? You got it: Embrace the diapers now because you'll surely miss them later on when you have to manage some yucky accidents. Diapers are so very easy, and I promise you that by the time they're in high school they will be out of them.

Now that you are hopefully on board with the diapers, here is a serious Hero Tool that will save the day, guaranteed. You and your spouse are both going to be champion diaper changers. However, even the best of the best parents will at some point end up with a baby with diaper rash. You can be doing a great job staying on top of it, but it's just part of being a parent, and it's one of the things that kids sometimes get. It took us two kids and more than a few diaper rashes to learn this next lesson. When you discover that your baby has a diaper rash and you treat it with diaper-rash cream, pay attention! If it is not getting better within a day and a half, then it is *not* a diaper rash. So what is it, you might ask? Think yeast infection! That is right, a yeast infection. A yeast infection is a fungal infection that grows in dark, moist places full of bacteria, just like diapers. Get a yeast-infection product or what we used, athlete's-foot cream, because athlete's foot is also a fungal infection. These creams start working right away to soothe your baby's rash.

BE AWARE, THOUGH, THAT WHILE A LASTING DIAPER RASH IS PROBABLY A YEAST INFECTION, IT COULD BE SOMETHING ELSE. THEY COULD BE ALLERGIC TO SOMETHING OR HAVE ANOTHER SKIN IRRITATION, SO IF IN A DAY AND A HALF IT IS STILL NOT LOOKING BETTER AFTER TREATING IT AS A YEAST INFECTION, THINK PEDIATRICIAN!

The danger in mistaking a yeast infection for diaper rash is that if you keep treating it incorrectly, odds are that it will get worse. Treated incorrectly, your baby could end up with a skin condition called impetigo quickly, which is very painful. The top layer of their skin will rub off and be raw and red so that when they poop, it burns the skin. The only thing to do then is hose them off with warm water, and it is heartbreaking. I don't want that to happen to your baby, so give diaper rash a day and a half max of treatment with a diaper-rash cream. If it's not visually getting better, change your direction and try treating it as a yeast infection. It'll save you and your baby a lot of heart-ache.

Another common place you may not suspect for your baby to get a yeast infection is around their neck. One day, you may look and see that the neck is looking red. They have been a little fussy lately, but nothing else seems to be wrong. A red neck could be your indication of a growing yeast infection. This happens especially when they are little and swaddled most of the time. When we feed them milk, it sometimes drips and drizzles down their cheeks and into the folds and skin under the chin and by the neck. It is dark and

moist under the chin while they are all bundled up, which is the ideal place for a yeast infection.

If you pay attention, you can swoop in and save the day with your athlete's-foot cream, soothe your baby, and be a hero!

You are now prepared for and ready to tackle phase one of soothing your crying baby, which is checking and changing the dirty diaper and its associated issues! Now that you have phase one down, let's address the second main reason that your baby could be crying: hunger.

If after surveying the scene you find that your baby's diaper is clean and he is still crying, your wee lad is probably hungry. Easy enough to find out if your baby needs to eat. If you have been home, then you may already know it's time for the baby to eat. If you just got home, you may walk in the door, drop your work stuff, and be handed a crying, hungry baby. Or it could be two a.m., your turn, and you hear the call of your hungry baby.

Let's first talk about feeding the baby in general. Later, we will cover feeding specifics and Hero Tools to make your life easier and for you to feel more confident about feeding your little petunia.

A very common question that comes up is about scheduling the baby. For the first day or two, you should know that your baby will be hungry every couple of hours, sometimes more. About every two hours, they'll want to eat, and then they will usually want to go back to sleep. After all, they did have an exhausting journey to get to you. After day three, they will start being more awake between feedings.

After that, working on scheduling the baby is a fantastic idea. I highly recommend it, because it helped us have more freedom. Having a schedule to lean on was comforting for us, and our baby thought we knew what we were doing. Some people are not into creating a schedule for the baby and just go with the flow when the baby is hungry; however, that approach lends itself to letting the baby run the show and your life, which is, of course, your choice.

Creating a schedule helps your baby to know what's going on and what they can expect. Consistency is hugely important in making babies and children feel comfortable and safe at every age. It also lets them know who's in charge from the beginning. Being in charge is a good thing because they are basically helpless; they are really looking to you for guidance and to believe that you know what is going on, because they certainly don't.

You may not either, but they don't know that! Scheduling the baby is also good for you because it offers a bit of structure to lean on as you are learning what is going on.

In the first couple weeks, it's really difficult to put a baby on a strict schedule. With the first baby, it's a bit more difficult since it is all new, and you two could be a bit overwhelmed. However, your baby will naturally be on a schedule. If you pay attention and watch the clock, you'll see that they will wake up every couple of hours.

Scheduling is Great, consider waiting four to six weeks to move to an official schedule to give your baby some time to eat when they are hungry. They have the rest of their lives to be on a schedule. If you guys are consistent, then your baby will fall in line. Try not to put too much pressure on yourself to get them scheduled the day they get home. It will happen!

One of the best resources for scheduling the baby is the book *On Becoming Baby Wise: Giving Your Infant the Gift of Nighttime Sleep,* by Dr. Robert Bucknam, MD, and coauthor Gary Ezzo. The main idea of the book is to follow an eat, activity, sleep schedule. The key concept of the scheduling system is that as soon as they wake up, they should eat first thing. Then, have them do an activity before getting them back to bed. It makes sense because that is what people do even as adults. We eat, we do activities, and then we sleep.

As your baby grows and develops, their waking hours will get longer, and then you increase the activities and time they play. The first day or two holding them and playing with them could be the activity because they get tired quickly. As their activities and wakeful hours get longer, that's when you introduce the play gyms and other cute, age-appropriate baby activities. The key to remember is eat, activity, sleep, which is the fundamental process of scheduling them, according to the *On Becoming Baby Wise* book, and it worked well.

What I loved the most about the book is that they spell out for you what you can expect at each particular age on how long they should be able to go between feedings. Knowing what your healthy baby should be able to do when it comes to eating and wakeful hours biologically gives you a guideline to follow when you are trying to spread out their feeding times. In two and a half to three months, you could be theoretically working on getting them to sleep through the night, which is amazing for you as parents, because with more sleep, you will start feeling human again.

Eventually, you might decide to take your baby out of your room before they are able to fully sleep through the night and while you are spreading out the feedings. That means potentially more restful sleep between feedings, but more work during the feedings, meaning you need to go to your baby's room instead of having her right there in your room.

When your baby does start sleeping through the night, your life begins again, and you will enjoy and appreciate your baby and life even more. You will have to earn it, though, by being tough and brave, because it is heartbreaking when you first start spreading out nighttime feedings and hear her cry. It was really diffi-cult for us the first two times. By number three, we just didn't want the other kids to wake up!

This is how Michelle and I did it. We read up on how long she should be able to go between feedings. For example, if we fed her at one a.m. and we were spreading out her next feeding from three a.m. to four a.m., when she would wake up looking for food at three a.m., we would set a timer for five minutes to see if she would go back to sleep or stop crying, before we went to her. We would wait it out, she would go back to sleep, and slowly the feedings would spread out.

Scheduling also helps with your freedom. If you are breastfeeding, your partner will most likely pump milk and freeze or refrigerate it, which will enable you to help with some of the feedings. Scheduling is also good for you to be able to go out on a date night when the baby is old enough and you feel ready. You'll have breast milk you can use to keep up the feeding schedule while you're gone.

If you are working on scheduling your baby, you really want to avoid playing with the baby at night. Again, remember that the baby is learning. If he learns that the middle of the night is playtime, it might seem like fun at first. However, you are going to want him to sleep through the night at some point. If he thinks nighttime is playtime, then getting your baby back to sleep will prove to be a more difficult task. Instead, use this time to spend quiet, intimate time together.

Let's talk a little bit about breast milk versus formula. First of all, there's no right or wrong answer. You know and I know several adults who were not breastfed and turned out just fine. Some women are unable to breastfeed due to interference from antidepressants, blood pressure medication, or another medication that helps them survive, or she may simply decide she doesn't want to. In that case, you both will feed your baby formula, and that's okay.

Formula today is probably the best it's ever been, with nutrients close to mother's milk. There are many different options in formula today, such as soy and other base-protein formulas. If you need to use formula for your baby, then you should know that it's going to be okay.

If your significant other is able and wishes to breastfeed, breast milk is a fantastic option. Her milk is made specifically for your baby and delivers immune properties, nutrients, and vitamins that can only be made by the woman who had the baby.

If you had a choice, then there are many great reasons to breastfeed. In the end, your partner is the one with the breast milk, and it is worth a conversation about your options, although supporting her and her decision will ultimately be healthiest for your child.

Now, let's get down to actually feeding your baby.

When feeding your baby, the first step is always to change the baby's diaper. After the baby eats and they're all snuggled up in your lap or in your wife's arms with a nice, full tummy, the last thing you want to do is disturb them by rustling around with a diaper. Whether your Hero Mom is breastfeeding and you're getting the baby for her, or it's your turn to feed the baby, change the baby first so that they can rest up after eating.

If your partner is pumping breast milk so that someone else can help with the feedings, the milk will need to be either refrigerated to be used soon or frozen to be used later. Freezing breast milk is an excellent way to have some reserves in case you go out, or in case she has a glass of wine and needs to dump a batch. However, any milk set aside in the fridge or freezer must be brought up to body temperature before feeding to stay consistent. That way, your baby will get what she is used to and not go bananas because she is used to a nice, body-temperature bottle of milk.

What you need to know, Dad, is that you cannot microwave breast milk to make it warm. The microwave will kill all of the good bacteria and nutrients that are in the milk. You will need to give the bottle of milk a water bath to bring it up as close as possible to body temperature. If you are feeding the baby formula, then you can microwave it and you are good to go.

Michelle breastfed our babies, but all of them had some formula now and again, so I had to heat up the milk. Allow me to share with you what I used to do, and then I will share with you the magic Hero Tool that will make the process a snap.

When Eliana, our first baby, who is now fourteen years old, was crying to let us know it was time to eat, I would go to the fridge or freezer, take out the milk, and start running the hot water in the sink. Anyone who has waited for the water to get hot in the middle of the night when the pipes are cold knows that it takes a little bit of time—okay, a lot of time—and with a crying, hungry baby it feels like forever. This went on for a long time until I figured out what you are about to learn.

Introducing boiling water to your baby's milk bottles will shorten the lag time between crying baby and happy, fed baby considerably. Enter the Hero Dad Thermos Tool: always have a thermos of boiling water ready to go at all times. Boil up some water, either on the stove or in the microwave in a microwave-safe bowl, and put it into a thermos. Whenever it is your turn to feed the baby, you will be set up for success day or night. If it is the daytime, simply pour your boiling water into a heat-safe bowl or container and drop the bottle or frozen bag of milk into the boiling water. You can also watch this Hero Tool video at www.The-HeroDad.com. If you are going to be feeding the baby in a few hours in the middle of the night, bring the thermos with boiling water to the place where you will feed your baby, along with the milk in a refrigerated or insulated bag with an ice pack. That way, when your baby cries in the middle of the night, your supplies are ready when you get there.

Now this is my disclaimer, and please read this carefully, because I want you to have a great experience. *You must check the temperature of the milk before you give it to your baby.* You must because the milk will heat up quickly. The water will be hot, and this system works, so you really need to be conscious of the temperature of the milk before you give to your baby. So again: After you give the bottle a water bath in the hot water, you want to check the temperature of the milk by squirting a few drops onto one of your wrists. The skin on your wrist is very sensitive and will tell you if the milk is too hot or needs another minute or so. Be careful here—after using this method a couple of hundred times, the milk never got hot enough to burn my wrist while checking the temperature, but be conscious when you take the bottle out of the hot water as to how hot it is. If your water is hotter than mine and the bottle is too hot to hold, let it sit for a minute before you squirt some on your own wrist to be on the safe side. After all, you have a crying baby who is hungry, and if you overheat the milk and give it to her without checking first, you could have a hungry baby with a burnt tongue, and she will be really pissed off, which is the opposite of what we want.

The milk will not usually get too hot, because when you put the cold milk bottle into the hot water, much of the energy will be used raising the temperature of the milk, and the heat dissipates rather quickly through the process and tends to leave the bottle at or close to the perfect temperature for feeding.

To heat the milk, there are other options; you also could buy a bottle warmer. However, that little contraption usually ends up in a landfill, so why spend the money when you can use a thermos? If you are careful, it works like a charm, and you can bring a thermos with you wherever you go. You cannot bring a bottle warmer with you unless you have a really long extension cord. A thermos you can use over and over again,

BREAST MILK PREP

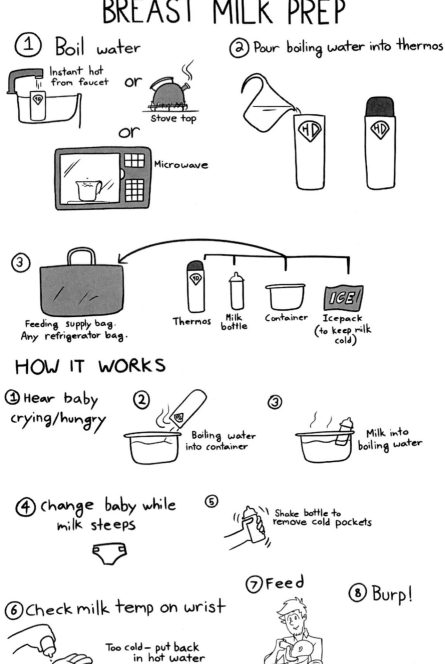

① Boil water

Instant hot from faucet **or** Stove top

or

Microwave

② Pour boiling water into thermos

③

Feeding supply bag. Any refrigerator bag.

Thermos

Milk bottle

Container

ICE
Icepack (to keep milk cold)

HOW IT WORKS

① Hear baby crying/hungry

② Boiling water into container

③ Milk into boiling water

④ change baby while milk steeps

⑤ Shake bottle to remove cold pockets

⑥ Check milk temp on wrist

Too cold — put back in hot water

Too hot — let cool

Most times → perfect, ready to go

⑦ Feed

⑧ Burp!

like when you are at your baby's soccer game five years later, holding your coffee.

Let's now put it all together. You get the wake-up nudge in the middle of the night and you know it is your turn. You go to where your baby is, and here is the sequence of events you can follow.

First, before you even go to the baby, dump the boiling water into the heat-safe bowl and then put in the milk bottle.

Second, you go and change your baby. Third, get the milk, which will already be heated up and ready to go. Fourth, shake the bottle to even out the temperature and get rid of any cold pockets. Fifth, test the temperature on your wrist. If it is not warm enough, put it back into the water for a minute. If it is too warm, shake it and let it stand for a minute. The temperature will be pretty close to perfect most times. Step six, snuggle in your favorite spot and feed your hungry offspring.

The next question I usually get is, how do I know if they are done?

Great question! If your partner is breastfeeding, remember breastfeeding is a supply-and-demand process. In the beginning, the amount of milk she is pumping should be the right amount for your baby.

Your baby is also very intuitive. They will eat until they are full and then they will stop (unlike adults with a bag of chips). If you are feeding your baby formula, the general rule is 2.5 to 2.7 ounces per pound of body weight. So, if your baby weighs six pounds (6 x 2.5 = 15), he should consume about 15 or 16 ounces of formula in a twenty-four-hour period. If he weighs ten pounds (10 x 2.5 = 25), he should have roughly 25 to 27 ounces in a twenty-four-hour period.

A serious key to having a good experience when you feed the baby is to burp them. Burping your baby is of paramount importance. How do I know that? Because I was not burping my baby for the first couple of weeks, and every time I fed her, she cried. To figure out what was going on, Michelle and I went over what I was doing step by step. We realized I wasn't burping the baby. No one ever told me I needed to burp her! I didn't read this book, so nobody told me and I just didn't know. So, I started burping the baby—problem solved.

You need to be kind of firm when burping the baby. It's not just a gentle tap, tap, tap—you want to be firm enough to get the job done, but you do not want to give him whiplash. Now when it comes to burping, there

BURPING STYLES

BURP FOR AT LEAST 15 MINUTES BEFORE PUTTING BABY DOWN

are several different techniques, but there's no one best way. There's only the way that your baby likes. You have the old-fashioned over the shoulder, which is a fantastic method that has been used for hundreds and hundreds of years.

This method is especially helpful in the beginning, when your baby doesn't have full control over their neck and their muscles are not yet strong.

You can also sit him on one knee, with one hand under his chin and the other hand on his back. Your hand holding under his chin should be shaped like you are holding cup. Be careful to have his chin, not his neck. Then pat his back until you get a burp. That's the way my kids always liked to be burped in the beginning. Another good way to burp the babies is over your knees. Babies love to be on their bellies, and it's also a nice way to hold the baby when you're eating. If you're at the table, you can hold the baby over your knees and pat his little back that way as well.

An important Hero Tool here is that they don't always burp right away, so how do you know how long is long enough? You want to burp them for at least fifteen minutes before you put them back down. Look, sometimes they burp right away, sometimes it takes five minutes, and sometimes it takes ten, but if you don't give it a good, fifteen-minute college try, it's not long enough.

If after fifteen minutes they do not burp, or if they did and you missed it, then it is pretty safe to lay your baby down to sleep. Anything less and you're really loading the dice against yourself. You will probably end up getting up again to deal with a crying baby with a painful gas bubble in the tummy. Absolutely do not forget to burp the baby. If mom is breastfeeding, it is fine to give junior a break and burp her, although unlike when you feed your baby a bottle, there are not really air pockets in a breast, and if they have a good latch onto her breast, they will not be sucking in any air and will have less need to burp.

On the subject of feeding the baby and troubleshooting a grouchy lad, here is another Hero Tool for you. Be conscious of the size of the nipples on your bottles. As your baby starts to get bit older—three weeks, a month, a month and a half—the quantity of milk they need will increase, as well as how fast they want it. If you guys are rolling along and everything has been cool, but then one day your baby begins fussing, consider whether you've adjusted the nipple size and flow of your baby's bottle. It may be time to get the next size and flow up. A lot of times, nipple flow is not what we are thinking about, but if you change the nipple to the next level, you very well can have yourself a happy baby again. You are the man, again! Ta-da!

When it comes to breastfeeding, you would think there is not much for you to do besides being supportive. However, there are ways to help your Hero Mom with the process. First off, be conscious that breastfeeding is not always as easy as we think it should be. I, for one, thought there would be nothing to it.

You take a baby, put it on the boob, and you're done, right? Wrong. There is a reason that there is a multi-million-dollar industry around breastfeeding, with products and coaches and support groups, because as it turns out, it is not always so easy for our ladies to get a rhythm down. Being conscious that the process can be difficult is a great start.

I asked Michelle, who successfully breastfed all four kids, for some tips to share with you and your significant other. For starters, ask your partner if she has a goal for the amount of time she will breastfeed. Michelle's goal was six months. You and your spouse might be thinking one year or one month, but Michelle works full time, so for us six months was a good goal. We agreed that if she could go longer, then she would. If your partner doesn't have a goal already, you can help her set one based on her situation and desire.

You can also share another lesson from Michelle's experience, and that is that it seems six weeks is the turning point for when things get easier. Of course, your partner might be a natural from day one, and that is fantastic. That doesn't happen for all women, though. If your partner is in the second group, you can assure her that if she really wants to reach her goal, hang on for six weeks and it will all get easier. If you ever find yourself in need of an extra hand, there are several great support and help groups. We called the La Leche League and they were awesome.

One huge way that you can help your breastfeeding partner to succeed is to help her stay hydrated. Hydration will significantly work for healthy breastmilk production, just as being dehydrated will really work against your partner's milk production. It's very important that she drink enough water every day to maintain and help with healthy milk production. You should know that hydration for a normal person, man or woman, is roughly equivalent to half their body weight in ounces of water daily. I know, it's bananas how much good, clean water we need for our bodies to function as they should. If you are a two-hundred-pound guy, you should drink close to one hundred ounces of water per day. Being properly hydrated will seriously increase your odds of feeling more energetic and less sluggish, and maybe even help you drop some pounds. Your odds will also be greater that your digestion, organs, and brain will be functioning as they should. Being hydrated also keeps your joints working and lubricated. Let's just say it is ridiculous how simply drinking enough water can help you to feel better and improve your general health and well-being.

Now translate all of those health benefits to your nursing wife. Besides all of her regular bodily functions that need hydration, add the fact she needs to be producing milk. Just think about it—when she's breastfeeding, a lot of the hydration is going to her milk production, and you want to help her replenish. You will find that after she feeds your baby, she is going to be thirsty. So, whether you got the baby for her or she did a solo mission, it is very helpful to get her a cup of water before she nurses to anticipate her thirst. Hydration has a lot to do with her milk production and could make the difference with breastfeeding, especially if she doesn't typically like to drink water. Pay attention—if she's having a bit of trouble and doesn't realize that she is not drinking enough water, you can mention, "Honey, I have noticed that you are really not drinking that much water, and I know it has a lot to do with milk production. Maybe you should try upping your water for a few days and see how it goes." If you figure her weight and cut it in half, she can calculate how many ounces or bottles or cups she would need per day and then just have them in the fridge, for example. It's a big deal, and you can shine here by helping her stay on track with the water. And look, if you guys figure out her target water consumption and come close, it is a lot better than not doing so. At the very least she will be upping her odds of success.

If your lady is breastfeeding, a pump makes life a lot easier. As we talked about before, the benefits of pumping are great for creating freedom, keeping a schedule, and being able to go out for a date, which you may want to consider at some point for mental health. These days, you can get a pump for free or nearly free with most insurance plans, so why not? The pumps usually last forever. Ours lasted through all four kids—you just need new tubes for each baby.

You should now hopefully feel pretty good about how to feed the baby and how to support your lovely lady through the breastfeeding process. I get asked often about when to introduce solid foods. It is a little bit down the road, but I'll go ahead and give you the skinny on solid foods.

There is no steadfast rule about when babies can start eating solid food; however, in general, solids are introduced when your baby is between four and six months old, depending on your baby's progress. The first solid foods to introduce are cereals, oatmeal, or rice cereal, which you would mix with a little formula or breast milk. After the cereals come vegetables and, last but not least, fruit. Fruit comes last because it has all the sugar, which they will like more than the vegetables. As they get teeth and start getting even bigger, you can start introducing more food groups. But in the very beginning, it's cereal, then vegetables, then fruit.

In the baby-food arena, it is easy to make yourself into a hero, my friend, and this is how: by making your own baby food. It is so easy and so good for the baby because you know what you're putting in there. Store-bought baby foods are inspected and healthy, but you know they are processed in a big plant. Michelle and I bought food all the time, but still, there is nothing like making your own food. When I did carve out time to make some food, it saved a trip to the store, time, and money, which is always nice.

If you decide to try and make some baby food, plan for a couple of hours worth of work tops. This is what you need, and most of it you may have already: a food processor or blender, some ice cube trays, and some gallon-size freezer bags.

Next pick out a vegetable. Let's say sweet potatoes for this example, but you could pick carrots, squash, or whatever you like, and even watch my video for more examples on how to make baby food.

THEHERODAD.COM/RESOURCES

Peel the sweet potatoes and chop them up into cubes. Then put them in a pot of boiling water and boil them up till they are al dente—soft, but not too mushy. So far, pretty easy. After you boil the potatoes, drain them in a colander. Next, put a little water in the bottom of your food processor or blender and add some potato chunks. The next part is the hard part. Get ready . . . press the pulse button on your machine. Seriously, that's it. Pulse the veggies while adding some water until you get the right consistency, which is smooth but not soupy. You may mess up a batch or two to get it right, but you will get it and still save a ton of dough.

Once you get the consistency the way you like it, spoon it into the ice cube trays and put them in the freezer. You can make a few trays of sweet potatoes, squash, carrots, peas, or mix and match. When it comes time to doing fruit, try apples, pears, mangoes, and bananas—it's all the same. The softer fruit, like mangoes and bananas, don't need to be boiled. Just chop them up with a little bit of water, and there you go.

When the cubes are frozen, dump the trays into a freezer bag, then write the contents and date on the outside. Now you have baby food made by your own hands in your own kitchen, and you can feel like a hero!

You now know how to take care of the big two causes of your crying baby. When you hear your baby calling you, you have a system in place. You will survey the scene and check the diaper, handle it, and if that does not do the trick, you will determine if they are hungry and remedy that situation as well.

If they have a nice, clean diaper, have already been fed, and are still crying, you can use this next set of amazing tools, compliments of the genius Dr. Harvey Karp.

In his book and DVD called *The Happiest Baby on the Block*, Dr. Harvey Karp explains a system to soothe your crying baby based on the idea that when your baby is born, it is like a fourth trimester. The first couple of months out and into your new crazy world, your baby—who was totally safe and happy bouncing around in Mama's belly—has now been delivered. Often the reason they cry is the same reason you and I sometimes want to cry: this life is stressful! For a baby, it's new, there are a lot of changes going on, and they're freaking out a bit. Dr. Karp created a set of tools to soothe your baby called the Five S's.

Dr. Karp's *Happiest Baby on the Block* changed my life, and I highly, highly recommend that you purchase his video and practice these tools. I will review his tools, but please support Dr. Karp, because there is nothing like having his DVD.

There's really no substitute for seeing Dr. Karp calm these babies. I didn't know about the Five S's until our third baby, and I struggled. The Five S's are Swaddling, Side, Shushing, Swaying, and Sucking.

Number one is Swaddling. Your baby just spent nine months snuggled up in a little ball inside your partner's belly, so we want to mimic that environment the best we can, and one of the best ways we can do that is swaddling. That's why any movie you see or any hospital you go to, newborn babies are swaddled up. Swaddling is super easy and I'm going to go over how to do it. The nurses in the hospital will also be happy to show you how to swaddle.

Dr. Karp's acronym for swaddling is DUDU, or down up, down up. All you really need is a rectangle-shaped blanket, just like the ones you get from the hospital, though any rectangular blanket will do. Do baby stores sell snazzy swaddling blankets? Yes, of course, and they have Velcro and straps, and they're fantastic and unnecessary.

In regard to swaddling your baby, the recent research shows that swaddling styles that are too tight could have a negative effect on your baby's hips and could cause hip dysplasia. Seems there is always something new to worry new parents about, but better safe than sorry! This means that you need to be careful to leave your baby plenty of hip space when swaddling him. The old-fashioned way is not recommended anymore, even though it works great and when done properly does not infringe on your baby's hips at all, because the blanket is wrapped around their torso, not their hips. Now there are two new ways for you to choose from that are approved to leave room for hip freedom of motion but are not as effective.

Here is the most recent "best method" to swaddle.[8]

---

8 "New Warning about Swaddling," International Hip Dysplasia Institute, accessed December 7, 2016, http://hipdysplasia.org/news/latest-news/new-warning-about-swaddling/.

NEW STYLE SWADDLING

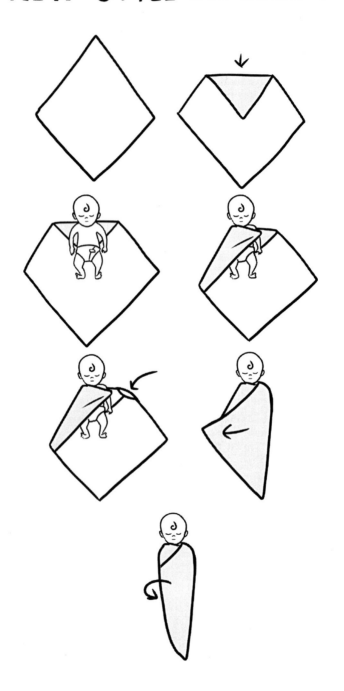

Both the diamond and square methods are essentially the same, except with the diamond method, you place the blanket with one corner up and "dog-ear" the corner as you would a book page. This is from the International Hip Dysplasia Institute:

1. If using a square cloth, fold back one corner creating a straight edge.
2. Place the baby on the cloth so that the top of the fabric is at shoulder level. If using a rectangular cloth, the baby's shoulders will be placed at the top of the long side.
3. Bring the left arm down. Wrap the cloth over the arm and chest. Tuck under the right side of the baby.
4. Bring the right arm down and wrap the cloth over the baby's arm and chest.
5. Tuck the cloth under the left side of the baby. The weight of the baby will hold the cloth firmly in place.
6. Twist or fold the bottom end of the cloth and tuck behind the baby, ensuring that both legs are bent up and out.[9]

---

9 "Hip-Healthy Swaddling: Are you swaddling your baby properly?" International Hip Dysplasia Institute, accessed December 7, 2016, http://hipdysplasia.org/developmental-dysplasia-of-the-hip/hip-healthy-swaddling/.

OLD-FASHIONED SWADDLING

① LAY OUT RECTANGULAR BLANKET

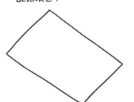

② DOG-EAR TOP CORNER

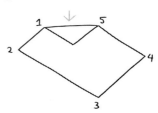

③ LAY BABY ON BLANKET, LEAVING 2 FINGERS-WIDTH OF SPACE BETWEEN TOP OF DOG-EAR AND SHOULDERS

④ FOLD CORNER 1 AT DOG-EAR OVER RIGHT SHOULDER

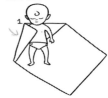

⑤A TAKE CORNER 2 TO LEFT TORSO

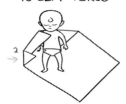

⑤B TUCK CORNER 2 AROUND LEFT TORSO BETWEEN ARMPIT AND TOP OF HIPS

⑥ TUCK CORNER 3 OVER AND BEHIND LEFT SHOULDER

⑦ WRAP CORNER 4 ACROSS FRONT OF BABY, BEHIND BACK, AND TUCK INTO TOP LEFT (CORNER 5)

⑧ ALL DONE!

This is the old-fashioned method, to give you all the possible methods:

1. Lay the blanket down in front of you.
2. Fold down the top right corner of the rectangle like when you dog-ear a book page.
3. Put your baby diagonally on the blanket with her head above the dog-eared corner and her feet toward the center of the blanket, making sure that her shoulders are two inches below the "dog-ear" fold.
4. Leaving the dog-ear folded, take the bottom right corner and wrap it over your baby's right shoulder and arm and tuck the corner of the blanket under the left side of your baby's torso, leaving her left arm free for now.
5. Take the bottom left corner and tuck over your baby's left shoulder and arm leaving plenty of room for your baby's hips and legs to move about. You might be asking where the baby's hands should be. You want to put them by her belly or down by her side.

6. After both shoulders are covered, the remaining blanket should be off to the left side and look like a tail.

7. Lastly, wrap the tail over the front of your little package and all the way around her back, and there should be enough to tuck the corner in the top of the swaddle.

One key to remember here is to make sure that the blanket is wrapped snugly around her arms and torso, leaving her hips free to move around.

A very common question is how long you should swaddle the baby for, and the answer is really dependent on your baby. I know several people that were able to swaddle their baby until eight to ten months, and some even longer. Meanwhile, some babies are done with the swaddling after a month or two and will break out of their blanket over and over.

When they keep breaking out, that's when you know they are done. However, if they break out during the day, you can still try at night, because it is comforting for them to sleep in a swaddle on their back. It is important to note that your baby does not need to be swaddled every moment they are awake. Swaddling is a tool for soothing your baby and getting them to sleep. It is healthy for your baby to be free to move their joints and limbs during their time awake.

Dr. Karp's second S is Side. After your baby is swaddled, pick her up so that her back is against you and she is facing outward. She should be looking out into the world, as opposed to picking her up facing you like you would during feeding. Dr. Karp is right on the money here. They really like being held facing out on their side. Turn her on her side looking out, and this is the amazing part—just like my babies, your baby is going to have a sweet spot, and you might not believe it as I'm saying it, but it is 100 percent true that they will have a special angle at which you tilt them on their side (let's say she is snuggled up in your left arm, her head by your elbow, looking out, with her right shoulder up). Your baby will have her special angle that she will love. You can angle that right shoulder a little bit forward or a little bit back, and you will find her special spot. Believe it or not, when you find her spot, it will be like flipping on and off a switch with the crying. Wait and see it to believe it—it's incredible the difference it makes when you find the correct angle.

While you have her on her side, enter the third S: Shushing. This is exactly what it sounds like—bring her ear up close to your mouth and shush her. The key here is to match her tone. If she is screaming, shush as loud as you can to match her tone. If she is crying at a lower tone, shush at a lower tone. You want to match her tone the best you can, and the baby will calm down and relax. The shushing helps to recreate some of the sounds experienced in mom's womb, which is similar to water swishing around—*shhhhhhhhhhhh*!

The fourth S is Sway. While all this is going on, sway with your baby in your arms. The motion is similar to the feeling of swishing around in your wife's belly when she got up and down during pregnancy. When she moved, the baby was moving with her. Your baby will like the rocking motion; it's very comforting.

The last S is Sucking. You would think it's easy to take a pacifier and put it in your baby's mouth, but babies have a tendency to spit them out. What you do then is the "takeaway." Your baby has a sucking reflex, which means they will naturally try to suck if something is in their mouth. If they spit it out, put the pacifier in their mouth and gently tug on it as you would if you were going to take it away. They will bring it back in and be soothed.

The thing about these tools is that some babies only might need one of the S's, while others need them all. Your job here is to try them and figure out which ones work best for your baby. These tools really work if you use them. This explanation just gives you the basics. For the rest, support Dr. Karp and purchase *The Happiest Baby on the Block*. You will be glad you did.

One last "S" that is helpful is Skin-on-Skin contact. You can try the same S's with your baby in a diaper and you bare chested. Especially if mom is breastfeeding and your baby is often snuggled up skin to skin while at her breast, skin on skin can help to sooth her while she is with you as well and can help even if mom is not breastfeeding. The closeness is comforting.

There are other tools and tricks to soothe your baby that people talk about, like driving around the neighborhood, which could work. Do you really want to get in your car in the middle of the night and go through the effort of putting your infant in the car seat and driving around? Let me know how it goes! The Six S's work and work well if you use them.

Reality unfortunately dictates there will come a time when the tools just do not work and your baby feels the need to cry. This does not always mean there is something wrong, it means she just needs to cry.

Sometimes, the unsoothable crying mixed with working all day out in the world or right there in your home, sleep deprivation, or feeling exhausted and frustrated because you tried all of your tools, could push even the best-intentioned person to the edge. I know this is true because unfortunately, approximately one to three thousand babies suffer from shaken baby syndrome in the United States per year, and is 100 percent preventable.[10]

NEVER SHAKE YOUR BABY - EVER!

-container

egg

shaking back and forth

smashed egg = baby's brain

---

10 "Shaken Baby Syndrome - Facts and Figures," October 2010, New York State Department of Health, https://www.health. ny.gov/prevention/injury_prevention/shaken_baby_syndrome/ sbs_fact_sheet.htm.

Shaken baby syndrome occurs when an infant is violently shaken by a caretaker. Imagine a Tupperware container with an egg inside. Now imagine violently shaking the container back and forth. That is SBS. Your baby's brain is smaller than her skull and is held in place with connective tissue. If your baby is shaken too hard, the connective tissue can break, letting her brain bounce around in her skull cavity, causing massive damage and oftentimes death. The children who do survive are left with irreversible health conditions, including but not limited to brain damage, hearing impairment, vision impairment, retardation, and seizures, just to name a few.

SBS happens over 75 percent of the time at the hands of men, and they're not necessarily bad guys. Most of the time, they're guys just like you and me who work hard, are trying to do their part, and perhaps didn't have the opportunity to read a book like this or to take a class and learn about what could happen if you lose your self-control.

I have a confession to make. I also know about shaken baby syndrome because I shook my eldest daughter. I thank my creator every day that I did not shake her hard enough to hurt her, and that I was exposed to what SBS is. I was totally unaware at the time. I was twenty-four, clueless, and I did not realize I could hurt her. The fact that I could have permanently impaired Eliana or worse is one of the main reasons for my passion to reach out to new dads and teach them, to prevent as many cases of SBS as possible.

Sometimes the crying is unbearable. It will inevitably happen that you'll try your best on three weeks of no sleep, and despite all your efforts, your baby will continue to cry. When it happened to me, I was holding her and wondering why she was crying. Was it just to make me angry? That is when I shook her. It is easy to say I should have known better, or that of course she wasn't crying on purpose. However, I was sleep deprived, exhausted, and most crucially, I did not have any tools to cope with the stress of being a parent. So, I shook her.

Because SBS is considered child abuse, let me share with you that child abuse is a real thing that is happening every day, and there is a real opportunity to stop it. Honestly, I sometimes feel like giving my kids a good, old-fashioned ass whipping. If there is a parent of a teenager who says differently, then they are probably lying. We have been working hard to raise kids we feel are definitely in the "good" range. They get paid to help around the house and do the work, the dishes, laundry; they help cook and pick up the house, they make good grades, have no major health issues, and listen most of the time. The point is that even when kids are "good" and "normal," they challenge you and push all of your buttons whenever they can.

It is easy to get frustrated with your kids. Even with coming from a relatively healthy home as a child, learning and developing self-control to manage them in a healthy, nonphysical way took work and takes work to maintain, especially as they get older.

WE ALL HAVE OUR "STUFF" WE DEAL WITH.

If you are coming from a home where there was abuse, or violence, you can help change the future of your children and partner in a positive way if you are conscious that it is an issue and if you want to stop the continuation of that behavior. If you feel like you need to beat up your baby, your kid, or your partner to show them you love them, please know there are other ways to show love. If you are conscious you have those feelings now, before your baby comes is a great time to start figuring out how to change your behavior. Imagine how awesome it would be if you chose to acknowledge your "stuff." You talk about it with your partner, and go see a shrink who understands family dynamics and can help you by giving you insight and tools to make a positive change in your life and for your family. What a gift that would be, what a hero you would be! Growing and making changes is all about being brave, about being the best version of a man you can be to help your family grow up in a healthy environment and not have to correct your stuff you dealt with from your childhood, whatever "stuff" that may be. Young children are the most vulnerable to abuse, with 47 percent of them being five years old or younger.[11]

When you think about it, though, you can see how it could happen. No one tends to bring it up when you are pregnant to bring down the excitement, but the truth is parenting may just be the hardest job there is if you choose to get in there and really parent. In the begin-

---

11 "Child Maltreatment 2014," Children's Bureau: An Office of the Administration for Children & Families, January 5, 2016, http://www.acf.hhs.gov/cb/resource/child-maltreatment-2014.

ning, your baby cannot even communicate in words, and you are tired and maybe caught up with a project at work, and you are helping with your baby and they can't exactly tell you what is going on. The stress could run high, and imagine you are a young couple, maybe even teenagers who are still not fully matured, who most likely have not taken any classes, read any books, and who may or may not have had positive parenting influences, or grew up with an abusive parent or influence. Without, maturity, self-awareness, or any tools, you can see how a person in that predicament could hurt their baby.

Thankfully, you now have no excuse! You are aware of SBS. If you are dealing with any "stuff" related to self-control and violent behavior, you are hopefully thinking about doing something positive about it to avoid the damage you can do and the pain you can cause. You have the Five S's Plus One to soothe your baby, and when those don't work, here's what you can do. If you find yourself getting frustrated with your baby, put her down and walk away! That's right, set her down in her crib and walk out of the room. At very least you will know that your baby is alive and well, screaming her head off in the next room. The next tool is to take three to five breaths. Taking three to five nice, deep breaths will help to relax your nervous system and signal your brain to relax whether you want to or not. That is how taking breaths works. Pretty cool! Once you have relaxed and feel you have yourself together, go back in and start again.

Two more tools for you here: First is to have a code or a signal with your partner that signals you are done, at your edge, and it would be safer not to handle your baby at that time. Our code was, in fact, "I'm done." When we really could not handle anything else, we would drop an "I'm done." When this was the case, it was our partner's duty to take over, no questions asked. Keep in mind that your partner can reach the edge as well. It is important to communicate in order to keep your baby safe and to keep you and your partner sane and on the same page.

Please, please never shake your baby, or hurt your partner!

The last tool is a little gold nugget to help you deal with your crying baby. It is a mantra or saying that came to me when caring for our third baby, Sarah. Whenever she would cry and it was my turn to manage and care for her, I would repeat to myself, "It's not her fault. Crying is the only way she can communicate. It's not her fault." That mantra grounded me before I went in to care for her, helping me by first reminding myself her crying is not actually her fault. If she could say, "Hey guys, I have a poop over here and I am quite hungry," she would have, and so would your baby! Starting off thinking and being conscious that the crying is not her fault helps in a big way to be calmer and handle the task at hand.

Men often ask about how to learn the different cries of your baby and how you can tell what exactly is wrong. If you are around and paying attention to your baby, you will learn their different cries. If you fed her and she stopped crying, that's the hungry cry. You will learn her different cries by participating and caring for your baby.

Knowing the cries of your baby is extremely useful and will help you identify when something out of the ordinary is going on. One day Michelle and I were downstairs and heard a bloodcurdling scream. We ran upstairs and Eliana had got her foot caught in one of the rungs of her crib. It was 100 percent different than any other scream that she had made before. If something is seriously wrong, most likely her screams will be in no way similar to her typical hungry, poopy, need-soothing cries. If there's a problem, you will know it right off the bat!

Hopefully you feel little bit more prepared for handling your crying baby. You now have more tools than most new dads. You have a plan, you have tools, and you are ready!

CHAPTER 5

POSTPARTUM

THE next topic we are going to cover is a very important one to understand, and that is your lady and the postpartum phase of birth. When we are done, you are going to have a handle on how long it should last, what you can expect, and how to help your lady through it like a hero.

The first thing you should know is that postpartum does not necessarily mean postpartum depression. Postpartum is simply what the phase after birth is called. Every woman will have a different emotional response during her postpartum time frame. Her emotional response could fall into one of three categories: baby blues, true postpartum depression, or postpartum psychosis.

If your woman typically has intense emotional issues around her period, then you may expect a few more postpartum issues. That's because when a woman has issues around her period, it's usually because her hormones are out of balance. After your baby is born, her hormones will go crazy trying to get back in sync and convert to mommy hormones that support milk production. If they were out of balance when she did not just have a baby, you may expect a little bit more in the unbalanced-hormone department. I'm not saying it's always the case. In some cases, her body could get realigned hormonally, even if in the past she had horrible periods. Her system could get rebooted, so to speak, as a side effect of the birth process, so after that she could have a much easier time during her periods.

Everyone tends to lump what happens chemically and emotionally with a woman as postpartum depression. However, what really happens with most women is considered baby blues. Baby blues are extremely common after birth, with 70 to 80 percent of new moms experiencing at least some signs of feeling down.[12] You can expect anything from two weeks to a little over a month of baby blues. During this time, she may feel sad and cry unexpectedly. Perhaps you might hear your wife saying things like "What did we do? Our life was so good before." Just know that your Hero Mom

---

12 "Baby Blues," American Pregnancy Association, last updated August 2015, http://americanpregnancy.org/first-year-of-life/baby-blues/.

is 100 percent entitled to some baby blues! Let's face it, she put on all of this weight, squeezed a baby the size of a watermelon out of her vagina, or had it cut out of her abdomen, and now she has the burden of getting back in shape, figuring out how to nurse the baby, figuring out the whole mommy thing, and also worrying about your involvement, because let's face it, many dads hardly help with raising their kids. They are a mommy all of a sudden, while dads are typically expected to be ding-a-lings when it comes to the baby. Society's views are definitely shifting when it comes to a father's involvement, yet women are expected to become professional mommies overnight by society and also self-imposed expectations!

The pressure of being a new mother can be very stressful, and this is not even taking into account the hormonal and chemical changes in their bodies. You can imagine that this postpartum phase is quite a transitional time, and it is clear why it would cause some sadness and maybe even a little mourning of your past life together, that last phase when you did not have a little baby's survival resting in your hands.

If the baby blues go on longer than a month and you see your woman changing in extreme ways, you should become concerned. If she starts becoming manic—cleaning voraciously, having bursts of unusual energy that are unusual for her—that's one sign of postpartum depression. Or it could be the opposite, like withdrawing and not being interested in your new baby's life, or not showing interest in feeding or caring for the baby. These are real signs and symptoms of postpartum depression, along with regular signs of depression. These include not taking care of herself, being tired all the time, or only wanting to lie in bed and hide under the covers. As a Hero Dad, it is under your job description to identify that she is having an issue and to say something and help her to take a positive action. Consider suggesting that you would be glad to make an appointment for her and go with her to her OB or midwife sooner than the next scheduled appointment together. Should I take off work to go? Yes! Take off. Do what you have to do to get the help she needs. If you find yourself in this situation, which is relatively common (one in seven[13]), then take the opportunity to be there for your partner, to support

---

13 "Postpartum Depression," American Psychological Association, accessed December 7, 2016, http://www.apa.org/pi/women/resources/reports/postpartum-depression.aspx.

her. Going through the ups and downs together helps build your strength as a couple, which is really important if you want to stay together for the long haul and parent your kids together.

Be conscious that sometimes a person who is truly depressed could say, "No, no, no. I'm really fine, just give me another day," or perhaps "Okay, you are right, I have been feeling down and will call myself." If she tells you that she will call to make an appointment, fine, help her by suggesting she call this morning or soon after your conversation, which may help her make the call. Be sure to follow up. You can check in during the day and ask her nicely, "Honey, have you had a chance to make that appointment?" It's really imperative that you help your partner get in to see a professional, because one or two women out of a thousand whose symptoms of postpartum depression are ignored could be experiencing postpartum psychosis.[14]

---

14 MGH Center for Women's Mental Health, "Postpartum Psychiatric Disorders," Massachusetts General Hospital, accessed May 18, 2016, https://womensmentalhealth.org/specialty-clinics/postpartum-psychiatric-disorders/?doing_wp_cron=1458072532.7822909355163574218750.

Postpartum psychosis is when a new mother is no longer of her right mind and can hurt the baby or herself. You've read the stories in the paper now and again about women who hurt their babies. Not long ago, there was a woman who drove her car into the ocean with her four kids in it. She had postpartum psychosis, and sadly nobody was caring for her. The condition is real, and I have personally met some men whose wives' PPD turned into postpartum psychosis. Sometimes they had an intervention and still fell off the edge. Be conscious because you do not want that to happen. Everything will change, you will have to take over all duties, and it is very sad for everyone involved.

Those are the different postpartum scenarios. Right now, you might be saying to yourself, "Please, let her only have baby blues!" You might also be asking yourself an important question. Hopefully that question is not "How fast can I get out of this mess!?" but "What is the best thing that I can do to help my partner through this transitional time?"

If baby blues turn into PPD, the best thing you can do is identify it early and get her in to see her doctor. If she does have actual postpartum depression, there really are a lot of options these days that you both can discuss and come to terms with. You could decide that a pharmaceutical solution is your answer to help get her system back in sync. However, there are natural alternatives as well. These days, there are plenty of holistic doctors and natural options that help with depression, if you don't want to go the drug route. If she's taking prescription drugs for depression, she might not be able to breastfeed because of their effects on the baby. The hero move here is to have open communication about what is going on in order to be part of the solution and to help the best friend you have in the world, your partner.

The best thing that you can do to help your significant other through baby blues, and even true postpartum depression, is what this whole book is about: getting involved with the baby from the beginning. If you're not involved, she is going to go into lock-down mode on red alert, unless my wife is the only woman to lock down in times of stress. In this case, she needs to make sure that this baby is going to survive. If you're not in it with her, or if that is what she perceives, and she feels like she is on her own to make sure that everything is taken care of, then that is what she will do. It absolutely will not help her through the baby blues. If you don't participate, you will definitely add to the baby blues instead of making it better. The hero puts in the effort and gets his hands dirty in the business of caring for his partner and his family on all levels.

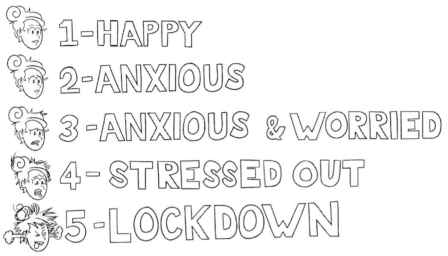

MOM'S LEVELS OF STRESS
1-HAPPY
2-ANXIOUS
3-ANXIOUS & WORRIED
4-STRESSED OUT
5-LOCKDOWN

Here is a Hero Tool to help you get involved: If you don't have one already, go get yourself a diaper bag. Pick yourself a backpack that you don't mind carrying around and turn it into a diaper bag. Bring it home without your partner asking. Show her that you're making an effort already to be involved and are ready to take an active part in your baby's life. There's a pack list on TheHeroDad.com of what you need to pack in your diaper bag to hook you up, of course. A few key items are a diaper-changing pad, first-aid kit, diapers, wipes, extra cloths, and an extra shirt for yourself, just to name a few. As soon as you and your partner decide that it's okay to bring the baby out of the house, you should incorporate your baby into the activities that you enjoy doing to give her a break.

If you work all week, then bring the baby with you wherever you go on Saturday or Sunday. If you want to go hit some golf balls, bring the baby. If you need to go to Home Depot, bring the baby. What you need to know is that taking your baby with you is a pain in the ass. It is a lot of effort to get everything you need together, put them in the car, and be aware of what they need, all to do a little of what you want to do. It is absolutely an effort! However, you wanted this baby and now you got it, so dad up and take the baby with you.

Even though it will be a lot of extra effort, few other things will make you feel as good as when you feel confident enough to take your baby with you and you get to hear, "Oh my God, what a great job! So nice to see a man out with his baby!" You will feel proud—and you should, because not every dad makes the effort to be involved, especially when they're young. More guys than you may think decide that they will get involved more with the baby when they get older and are better able to communicate.

The truth is, when your baby is young, you give a lot of effort and get a lot of poopy diapers to get rid of. That's just the way it is. That's one of the other things besides the sleep deprivation that makes the first few months challenging; you give and give and give, and you're not getting much back. You are also not getting much loving from your wife, because she's stressed out doing the same thing you are. It's really a selfless time when you're a new parent.

WHAT WILL HELP YOU THROUGH IS REALIZING THAT THE TIME AND EFFORT YOU ARE PUTTING IN NOW IS AN INVESTMENT.

Getting involved early will help you to bond with your new baby and with your partner on this new level, which will be the groundwork for the years to come. If you choose to put in the effort and support your partner emotionally through baby blues by helping her to feel reassured that you two are in this together, know you are doing your job and you are strengthening your relationship.

And it goes both ways. There will come a time when you want to see your buddies, to have a break, or go take a walk by yourself to clear your head. More and more men are revealing that they have been experiencing baby blues and depression. Having a baby is a huge deal—life changing. Men have feelings. We are all supposed to be tough and hard, but the meaning of tough is changing.

ACKNOWLEDGING HOW YOU FEEL TAKES GUTS. DEALING WITH YOUR "ISSUES" TO GROW AS A PARENT, PARTNER, AND AS A PERSON TAKES REAL STRENGTH. IF YOU ARE DEALING WITH EMOTIONAL STUFF AROUND THE BIRTH OF YOUR BABY OR WHEN YOU WANT A BREAK, IF YOU PAY IT FORWARD AND ARE THE FIRST ONE TO GIVE HER A BREAK OR TAKE CARE OF THE BABY WHILE SHE IS OUT WITH FRIENDS, SHE SHOULD BE HAPPY TO RETURN THE FAVOR. YOU WOULD HAVE ONLY GIVEN YOUR PARTNER GOOD REASONS TO RECIPROCATE AND BE THERE FOR YOU AND GIVE YOU A BREAK.

Early on, when everything is new and she's really relying on you to be there, show her that she can trust you. Your involvement will extend far beyond the baby blues. If she can count on you out of the gate, you will earn her confidence, and that will go a long, long way. If you keep up the effort, it will prove to be a nice way to live.

CHAPTER 6

HEALTH AND WELLNESS

UNDERSTANDING health and

maintaining the wellness of your new child is very important and can sometimes can be scary. Most new parents are rightfully nervous, because like it or not you are now responsible for the health and wellness of your new child, and you may or may not have had any medical, emergency, or even general health and wellness education.

Let's get you better prepared by helping you to understand what healthy means, which will help you make the best judgement call you can in the event of a health issue or emergency situation. To do that we will cover:

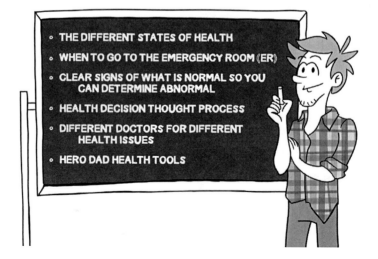

- THE DIFFERENT STATES OF HEALTH
- WHEN TO GO TO THE EMERGENCY ROOM (ER)
- CLEAR SIGNS OF WHAT IS NORMAL SO YOU CAN DETERMINE ABNORMAL
- HEALTH DECISION THOUGHT PROCESS
- DIFFERENT DOCTORS FOR DIFFERENT HEALTH ISSUES
- HERO DAD HEALTH TOOLS

When it comes to general health and wellness in the absence of a genetic or inherited disease, there is the state of wellness, which is more than the absence of disease, but the optimal state of balance between our physical, emotional, and chemical/hormonal health— our normal state of being and usually the condition your baby will arrive to you in. Then there is the state of sickness or dis-ease, which is when something is affecting the balance of health in our body, which will usually produce symptoms and is typically not an emergency to begin with. Then there are traumas and boo-boos like a fall or accident, which also may or may not be an emergency. Then there are true medical emergencies.

The most common concern and question when it comes to the health of your new little dumpling is, How do I identify a true emergency, and when do we to take our baby to the emergency room? First step in deciding the course of action is to survey your scene. Identify the signs that you have an emergency on your hands, and then take action.

Here are some common examples of possible emergencies and actions:

- Unconsciousness or unresponsive: Call 911 and start CPR if you know how
- Troubled or shallow breathing: call pediatrician or ER
- Trauma, like a fall or drop: call pediatrician or ER
- Seizure: call 911
- Accident causing bleeding that won't stop: call 911
- Vomiting or diarrhea for prolonged time: call pediatrician or ER
- Fever with a rectal temp of over 100.4 in infants younger than two months: call pediatrician or ER
- Crying that will not stop and gets worse if you pick her up, especially after an accident: call pediatrician or ER
- Allergic reaction affecting breathing: call 911
- Change in temperament: Monitor, and call pediatrician[15]

---

15 Cynthia Ramnarace, "Should You Take Baby to the Hospital?" Parents.com, March 2006, http://www.parents.com/toddlers-preschoolers/health/sick-toddler/should-you-take-baby-to-the-hospital/.

These are some common reasons that most new parents bring their children into the ER. These are general signs of true emergencies, although there could be any number of other unique emergency situations that could happen. If you and/or your partner believe you are experiencing a true emergency even for a nanosecond and believe you should be bringing your child to the emergency room or calling 911, you should go or call. Listen to your gut, and never take a chance unless you are by profession an emergency-room doctor and you know exactly what is going on and how to handle it. Why take a chance? You will get to the point when you will feel more confident about making decisions in the event of an emergency, accident, or boo-boo, even if you are not an ER doctor. In the beginning, it is better to err on the side of caution and take the trip.

In the big picture, making the trip to the ER is in a way cutting your teeth and giving you some real mom-and-dad emergency experience that there is just no other way to get. Visiting the ER is a rite-of-passage experience, and many times, you will find that nothing is seriously wrong with your little petunia. It is human nature and good for you to be overly cautious if you perceive that your family and baby are in harm's way.

There are times that if you don't err on the side of caution, there can be serious repercussions.

Once you do go to the emergency room a couple of times and get to fill out the insurance paperwork, wait sometimes for hours holding your crying child, and then finally see who knows which doctor to get your child the care they need and find out whether it was indeed an emergency or not, you will start to be more tempered with your decision to make the trip or not.

You might be thinking, *How do you know that we will have to make a trip to the ER?* Good question, my friend. Okay, I do not know for sure that you will have to go, and if it were in my power I would make sure that you would never need to bring your little poopsy to the emergency room or have any health issues at all. That is not the reality, and getting you prepared is what this book is all about, so you should know that the odds are in your favor that at some point you will end up in the ER with your child.

If you find yourself in an emergency room for any reason, ask questions and make sure the doctor is who he or she says they are. When Jonah was about seven, we took him to the hospital for our first (and hopefully last) broken bone—his arm. When the orthopedic doctor came into the room, Michelle asked to see his ID badge. He said no one ever asks to see his ID and it was an excellent question to ask. He told us that whenever you are in a hospital setting, it is a good idea to ask to see the doctor's badge to see if they are who they say they are and not a janitor moonlighting as a health professional.

Any time you believe something is not "normal" with your child's health, it is always a good idea to give your pediatrician a call, because if they are familiar with your baby they may be able to help you to be calmer by giving you some specific instructions on what you can do on the way to the ER or if you should call an ambulance, or they may have some insight into your experience and will help you decide if you are in the middle of an emergency or not.

Now that you have an idea of what an emergency looks like, let's talk about what "normal" looks like. Normal looks a little different in every baby, and your baby will clearly show you their unique, individual personality and demeanor. When it comes to what is normal in terms of health, thinking of your baby as a small human being instead of "a baby" or "infant" may help you to keep things in perspective, because after all, that's exactly what they are.

Listed below are some signs of the most common state of human health, "normal":

- Being hungry and wanting to eat on a regular basis
- Peeing and pooping several times a day
- Being alert and interested in what is going on when awake
- Tired after an activity
- Sleeping when tired
- Crying is normal, and the way your baby can communicate with you that they need something
- Breathing should be easy and unlabored
- Consistent body temp
- Consistent temperament
- Vomiting and diarrhea
- Fever

Most of these "normal" signs may seem like no-brainers, like your baby's desire to eat and that they should be able to breath easily. You may not understand why fever, vomiting, and diarrhea are on the "normal" list. Here is a little insight from a different perspective:

sometimes what we think of as "sick" actually means "healthy." Having a fever is, in a way, a good thing for your baby to have. The normal temperature for your baby is between 97 and 100.4 degrees Fahrenheit, or 36 and 38 degrees Celsius.[16] Anything above this is considered a fever. The best way to check your baby's temperature is rectally, because their ears are too small to get an accurate temp from. Yes, you need to stick the thermometer in your baby's tush!

You should know that a fever is a totally normal and healthy response for a human being, infant or fully grown, to have when they are fighting off an infection or something your body identifies as not welcome. When you spike a temperature, it means your body is fighting and doing what it is supposed to.

IMAGINE YOUR BABY HAD AN INFECTION AND DID NOT SPIKE A TEMP! THAT WOULD MEAN THEY ARE "SICK," AND THAT WOULD BE BAD.

Your baby is being exposed to new germs in her new environment all the time, and the body's natural response is to raise the temperature. Their white

16 BabyCenter Editorial Team, "Fever in Babies," BabyCenter, July 2015, http://www.babycenter.com/0_fever-in-babies_84.bc#articlesection1.

blood cells are activated and their bodies are building immunity. Fever is not always the enemy, as long as it's under control and doesn't keep rising.

We are not talking about spiking a 104-degree fever that lasts two days. It is important to understand what a fever means to help keep you calm. If your baby is under six months old, always err on the side of caution and call your pediatrician to get their input. My intent here is for you to understand that a fever is not "bad" per se. It is actually good that your baby's body is responding normally. Similarly, puking and diarrhea are also healthy responses to something not agreeing with your baby. We are not talking about continuous projectile vomiting or unrelenting diarrhea, just a bout of either in general. These bodily responses really should not be considered "bad" and do not always mean they are "sick." These conditions are simply an indication that your baby's body is healthy enough to identify something it does not like and wants to get rid of. Like the old saying, better out than in!

If you have a healthy baby without any diagnosed illnesses or conditions of note and she has a fever, pukes, or has some diarrhea, be alert, cautious, and keep a close eye on her.

 ALTHOUGH YOUR FIRST INSTINCT WITH THESE SEEMINGLY ABNORMAL FUNCTIONS IS TO THINK SOMETHING IS WRONG, TRY AND KEEP IN THE BACK OF YOUR MIND THAT YOUR BABY IS HAVING A NORMAL RESPONSE TO A HEALTH ISSUE.

Understanding what functions fever, vomiting, and diarrhea serve can help you to be calmer if and when it happens, as painful as it is when our babies are not feeling well.

You now have an idea of the states of health of a human being and the key indicators of what an emergency looks like, as well as what "normal" functions are, so you can better identify *ab*normal signs that may require medical attention.

Put your knowledge into action. Think SENT:

- Survey the scene
- Emergency or not
- Normal or not
- Take action

When our oldest daughter Eliana was maybe three and a half, we noticed that one day after preschool she was lying like a lump on the couch. Surveying the scene, Eliana seemed more than after-preschool tired, but completely spent. Her breathing was shallow and labored. It did not seem normal. When we got her to the ER, Eliana's oxygen was way down. It turned out she had developed reactive airway disorder. This is not quite asthma, but she had a "reactive airway," which means that when she got a cold or if her lungs got irritated, her lungs and bronchioles would overreact and constrict her airway. Whatever it was that triggered her that first time, we still do not know, but at that moment it was not as important as getting her to safety. Eliana could have died that day. That was our first experience with the emergency room. Surveying the scene and identifying she was not alert and had signs of labored breathing helped us to take the right action, which was going to the ER in this case, and thank the creator we went, because otherwise we wouldn't have Eliana here today.

Here is a Hero Dad perspective on doctors in general for you to consider. Doctors that you use for your family are simply tools in your tool kit, and when it comes to fixing a problem, you want to use the right tool for the job. Having a good pediatric practice that

you trust is very important, as they are usually ground zero for general health checkups, colds, school and camp physicals, and referrals out to any specialist you may need to see.

If you do have a health issue on your hands, a solid hero tactic that your baby will appreciate is for you to consider starting with the most natural remedies before moving to more invasive, less natural ones.

If you have never used one, chiropractic is another good tool for your family's health tool bag. I feel especially qualified to speak here because of my ten years of chiropractic clinical practice. My real passion is helping to create healthier, happier families by inspiring new dads to get involved with their partner and kids from day one. Taking the opportunity to take care of my family full time and teaching my new-dad class makes me a lot happier than filling out endless notes and dealing with insurance companies ever did. Life is too short. With that being said, I want you to benefit from inside information. This is NOT meant to be a sermon on how chiropractic can heal all ailments and is the end all be all, because it is not. Chiropractic is one of the best secret tools you can have in your toolbox when it comes to general health and wellness for your family.

Today, every MD and doctor show on the planet preaches about living a healthy lifestyle, with exercise, eating right, and taking care of your body as the best way to maintain the state of good health. That health concept is what chiropractic care was founded on. Consider thinking of chiropractors as mechanics for people. We humans have a structure with moving parts and pieces such as bones, joints, muscles, and ligaments. Sometimes the pieces get jammed and out of balance, which can cause a whole cascade of issues that can cause pain and cause a shift from the state of good health, which no one likes and is no fun.

Many baby and small-child issues can be physical in nature. Just think about it. Your baby started off by getting squeezed out of a very small space, which could twist one up a bit, which you know if you watched your baby be delivered. As they start getting bigger and stronger, they push themselves up and then fall down over and over again. Then they start creeping and crawling and then toddling, during which time they are falling and bumping themselves on the walls, the floor, and every other surface in your home. As they grow even bigger and enter the playset phase, your little one will inevitably fall off the swing and crash down off the slide, and it goes on and on.

If you take anything with moving parts and pieces and bang it over and over again, sometimes gently sometimes not gently, the parts and pieces will get knocked out of balance and simply will not function at their best. The moving parts and pieces of your child's frame, all of his bones and muscles work the same way! The falls and bumps of childhood easily could create an imbalance, which could show up as crawling in a weird or unbalanced way, an ear infection, constipation, colic, or the common cold, just to name a few. These are all very common side effects that can be caused by physical imbalances—not all of the time, but a lot of the time. It's hard to fix a mechanical issue with antibiotics or drugs, but a little adjustment might do the trick.

Do you really think your perfect little baby is missing a laboratory-made laxative or reflux drug? Does it maybe make more sense that her system could be a little out of balance and could benefit from a little gentle realignment after her crazy delivery into this stressful new world?

I would be remiss not to share the benefits of chiropractic care with you as a Hero Tool for your family health tool bag. There is a reason 69 percent of children who receive regular chiropractic care have never had an ear infection.[17] Today, with the major shift in "health care" to a more wellness, prevention-based model, chiropractic is more mainstream. It is not magic and does not fix everything. There will be many times your child very well may need an antibiotic or other medical remedy, and thank goodness they are there. It is nice to know there is a noninvasive, gentle, non-drug alternative to at least try when you find your child has fallen out of her natural, healthy state.

When it comes to your family's health, remember to be conscious of all treatments that are available. Today, drugs and invasive procedures are readily available for your family. Wouldn't it be better, though, not to need them? No matter which health provider and methods

---

17 Wendy M. van Breda, DC, and Juan M. van Breda, DC, "A Comparative Study of the Health Status of Children Raised under the Health Care Models of Chiropractic and Allopathic Medicine," *Journal of Chiropractic Research* 5, no. 4 (Summer 1989), 101–103. Also available online in pdf form at http://www.drschluter.com/wp-content/uploads/2013/02/VanBredaStudy.pdf.

you choose for your family, it is always a good idea to be conscious of your options, monitor the results, and if you are not seeing improvement, make a change. Seek another opinion and try another direction.

New dads often ask about picking family physicians. Many times, men report that their wives pick the doctors because they are the ones who bring the children most of the time. It is not a bad idea, however, for you to go and meet the people who will be caring for your baby. What if you need to bring your child one day and you don't have a good feeling about the place? It is much harder to switch after you start going to an office.

It is good to date a few offices and think about things like, What is the distance from your home? How long is the wait typically? Do they have healthy and sick waiting areas? Are there any other specific qualifications that you are looking for?

On the concept of starting with the least invasive tools and moving to more invasive tools when needed, let me share a Lila health story. Lila, our youngest, was always a snorer. When she was about a year and a half old, we noticed that the snoring was getting really bad.

It sounded an awful lot like she would stop breathing sometimes, and when you hear your baby stop breathing, it is very unsettling. After looking in her throat, it was clear that her tonsils were swollen. We brought her to our pediatrician, and they recommended surgery. We went to a specialist, who gave us the skinny on how the surgery would go. We decided to at least try a natural remedy, so we got her adjusted and went to a naturopath, which is essentially a natural version of a pharmacist, to see if there was something to bring the tonsil swelling down. It worked for a while and then stopped working, and we decided to have the surgery. We liked and had faith in our surgeon, and everything turned out fine. She could breathe again and was much happier, and we were so glad we had her tonsils removed. My point is that it never hurts to try a natural approach, because sometimes that approach will win, and you will be able to avoid more invasive approaches. However, sometimes you will need the more invasive tools, and thank goodness they are available to us.

Next let's take a look at some general health, wellness, and emergency Hero Tools that will serve you as you navigate through the different states of health. First, let's talk about pee and poop. Is it not amazing how much better you feel after you go to the bathroom? The reason is you are getting rid of waste your body no longer needs. It's the same for your little peanut. They should be going regularly. Pee and poop are actually really good indicators of health and wellness, and you can monitor them to check in on your child's health as they grow.

PEE SHOULD BE ALMOST CLEAR. THE DARKER THE PEE, THE MORE DEHYDRATED YOU OR YOUR CHILD IS, AND IT SHOULD BE ADDRESSED BY DRINKING WATER.

Children love to drink soda and juice and other drinks that often will leave them dehydrated. Your kids will not remember to flush the toilet for a good long while, so you might as well take advantage of the opportunity to check in on their hydration and make sure they are getting enough water.

Surprise! You can also tell a lot about your child's state of health from their poop. Their first poop is a thick, tarlike poop called meconium and will move to a more yellowish poop if breastfed, and then to the familiar, beautiful brown color when they move to solid food. As your child gets a bit older, you will find a great many poops in the toilet after they leave the bathroom. Yes, take a look before you flush it down. Is it solid, floating, fluffy, hard, mush, little pebbles, green, diarrhea? Yes, it is gross, but poop will also give you an indicator of their intestinal health, which has a huge impact on their overall health.

IF IT DOES NOT LOOK "NORMAL"—LONG, FLUFFY, AND SOLID—EVALUATE THEIR DIET AND CONSIDER CHECKING IN WITH YOUR DOCTOR.

Another tool is to be conscious of your baby's symmetry. How does she look on her left compared to her right? She should be pretty even, although know that no one, not even your perfect petunia, is exactly symmetrical. Normally, though, she will be pretty close. This is important and will come into play when your baby starts to move. She will first start to creep, which is a one-side-at-a-time movement, similar to a crab crawl, that uses one side of the brain at a time. Then she will start to crawl, which integrates her left and right brain to move each side in unison. If you notice that one side is not moving symmetrically or one side does not seem the same as the other in smoothness of movement or strength, or that she is dragging one leg, it could mean a number of things. For this type of situation, consider visiting your pediatric chiropractor to see if it is as simple as getting her a little adjustment. A certified pediatric chiropractor is an expert in structure, function, and movement and will be able to determine if it is a misalignment or something more serious like a neurological issue that is not in their scope, and will refer you to the appropriate physician. Hopefully an issue like this would only need an alignment to remedy.

When I was a kid, my dad Jerry saved two different people by administering CPR. His heroism motivated me to be able to do the same, and I learned CPR. With a small amount of training, you could be in the position to save a life also—talk about being a hero! Knowing CPR is paramount because if your child is in cardiac arrest and you dial 911, chances are they will not make it in time. Take the time to at least learn infant CPR. If you do, you will also learn how to help your baby if she is choking, which is an even more common occurrence with small children.

Your baby's risk of choking shoots way up as he starts crawling and eating solid foods. When your baby starts to crawl, he will put any and everything he finds in his mouth to help figure out what it is. This next Choking-Prevention Tool, you will not learn in a class, and it has not been approved by any agency, though Michelle and I have used this move several times. This Hero Tool is for when your baby is old enough to be in a high chair and eat regular food. There will come a time when she puts a piece of food in her mouth and is not quite choking yet, but you see that she is about to. As small as you cut up that hot dog, there will come a time when they make that face, the holy-crap-the-food-went-down-or-is-about-to-go-down-the-wrong-pipe face. On several occasions, that has happened, and one of us has picked the baby up and simply turned her upside down to let gravity do its thing. If you catch "the face" quickly enough, the piece of food usually will fall out. Sometimes it is too late and you need to do a bona fide choking procedure taught in your infant CPR course.

There is a PDF you can download from TheHero-Dad.com demonstrating some of the basic choking procedures you can administer. However, there's

THEHERODAD.COM/NEW-PARENT-GUIDES-DOWNLOADS

no substitute for taking a class and getting certified. Having a CPR chart up in your cupboard is also a good idea. If you stay calm and look at the steps on the chart, even without training, you could save a life.

This next tool works really well and comes in very handy: having red dish/burp towels in your kitchen. Why red towels? Because when a person bleeds, we tend to freak out. When you have a child that is bleeding, you could have a kid and set of parents who are freaking out—not good. But if your baby bangs her lip and you use the red cloth to compress the wound, there tends to be less freaking out, and you buy yourself a little time to assess the situation. Keeping one in your backpack or diaper bag for trips to the playground is also a good idea. It considerably lessens the freak-out factor.

Another good tool to be conscious of that something could be up with your kid is a change in their attitude. Lila is a typical fourth kid and is usually very easy and happy, happy, happy. When she was about three years old, she started acting super crabby without any real signs that anything was wrong, which was out of character for her. It just so happened that we needed to get Lila a physical for her preschool, so I took her in to our pediatrician.

When they looked in her ears, she had a huge ear infection. Yes, even a chiropractor's kid sometimes gets an ear infection. She wasn't pulling on her ears or lethargic, and she was eating, drinking, peeing, and pooping. She was not displaying any outright symptoms of an ear infection. Lila's attitude change was really the symptom of her not feeling well. Lila was three, but even from the time your baby is an infant, your child will not be able to articulate how they are feeling, and it can show through in their attitude even if there are no clear symptoms anything is wrong. Up to this point, we have covered many topics around health and wellness: the states of health, ER visits, normal signs of a healthy person, and a thought process and tools to assess your child's health, as well as the idea of keeping an open mind when it comes to your choices of resolving different health issues that may come up for your family.

Genetics, accidents, and emergencies aside, the most powerful influence on your family's health will be you and your partner. When it comes to health, your baby has no idea what "healthy" behavior, food, attitude, or rest is unless you show them. Once they move away from breast milk or formula to more real food, they will eat what you give them. They will exist in the world you create for them. Having a baby is a great time to make some "healthy" changes, because it is not just you anymore you are caring for.

 CONSIDER THIS. EVEN IF YOU CANNOT GIVE YOUR BABY A MILLION-DOLLAR TRUST FUND, YOU CAN GIVE THEM PERHAPS THE MOST VALUABLE GIFT OF ALL, WHICH IS GOOD HEALTH AND A STABLE HOME, SO THEY CAN GO AFTER THEIR DREAMS.

According to the American Heart Association, childhood obesity is the number-one heath problem in the United States—one in three kids are overweight or obese.[18] Everyone is working hard and we are busier than ever, and everyone is talking about the kids and what should we do about the kids. We should start with us, the parents, taking responsibility for our kids and what we feed them. We are busy and it is not easy; however, who is going to the grocery store? Your two-year-old? You can take an active role in helping your child live a healthier life. You, Dad, can use the tool of communication and talk about what kind of diet you and your partner want to feed your family.

You can give your child an edge in life by feeding them a healthy diet. If your child develops type 2 diabetes, it is your fault, plain and simple. If you allow for an unhealthy diet for your child, you are also helping to increase his risk for self-esteem and negative body-image issues, which could be avoided. It is hard enough raising kids today with all of the content they are exposed to even when you are watching and monitoring what they see. You are starting with a healthy baby. Work together to keep him that way!

---

18 "Overweight in Children," American Heart Association, July 5, 2016, http://www.heart.org/HEARTORG/HealthyLiving/HealthyKids/ChildhoodObesity/Overweight-in-Children_UCM_304054_Article.jsp#.WBipFy0rL3g.

Your influence on your child's health does not end with what you feed him. Your child's health will greatly be influenced by your relationship with your partner, how you speak, treat, and especially how you react to each other and your baby.

YOUR BABY IS WATCHING, LEARNING, AND TAKING CUES FROM YOU FROM THE MINUTE SHE ARRIVES.

When it comes to accidents and boo-boos, she is looking to you 100 percent of the time to see what her reaction should be. From her first fever to the first time she falls and scrapes her knee while she is starting to walk, she's going to look to you and your partner to see how you are reacting. If you get nervous easily and tend to freak out, that's okay. There's no right or wrong. Being able to stay calm can be learned and gets easier with experience. If being more centered in your reactions is less important to you, try to not be surprised when your child also freaks out when she scrapes her knee.

There's a fantastic book called *The Blessing of a Skinned Knee* by Wendy Mogel. It's all about letting your kids learn from painful experiences and giving them the freedom to figure things out for themselves, which will help them to become more resilient. I'm by no means saying to let your infants get hurt and figure it out on their own, but you will blink your eyes and your baby will be a year old, toddling around, and you'll be at the point where you need to decide how you want to react.

The way you choose to react to your experiences with and around managing and raising your children will set the tone for how you will live your life. Do you want to have a chaotic and reactive home life, or a more balanced one? Much depends on how you react to the experiences you will soon encounter. In most situations, the calmer you can stay, the higher the likelihood that the outcome will be closer to the one you want, because you will be able to survey the scene, figure out the problem, and go toward the solution you think is best, whether it means changing your family's diet, getting the keys to go to the ER in an emergency, calling the pediatrician, or simply getting a Band-Aid.

One example of when staying calm helped me avoid an ER trip was when our son, Jonah, was about three. He peed in his undies before preschool, and I sent him upstairs to get changed. I heard him running down the hall and then—*splat*. He came downstairs covered in blood from head to toe. I was about to freak out, but I surveyed the scene and realized he was covered from top to bottom, so it was obviously not a wound on his foot. He had tripped and hit his head on the corner of the wall in our hallway. I put him in the shower and hosed him down, and by the time I took him out of the shower, the bleeding had stopped. I put a Band-Aid on and he was good to go. Keeping my cool in this situation saved me a trip to the emergency room.

When you add a child into your world, life gets more complex and things happen. The more control you have over yourself, the more you can control your reaction to and influence over the direction and flow of health and everyday life in your home.

Our health and the health of our family is at the core of everything we do—without our health, there is not much we can do. Hopefully you feel a little better and more confident now that you have an idea of what you may expect and have tools you can use to help you assess issues as they come up, as well as an understanding that bumps and bruises come with the territory of having a baby in the house.

CHAPTER 7

SAFETY AND BABY-PROOFING

ON to safety! When it comes to safety and bringing home a new baby, one of the most common questions and concerns is how to introduce a dog or cat to a new baby.

Let's start with dogs. If you love having a dog in the house, I am with you. A lot of how your dog will react to your new addition depends on her personality. Dogs are pack animals and understand the hierarchy of a pack. Your dog will be going from being third in the pack to fourth in line for attention. Our dog, Sasha, went from being third in our pack, to fourth, and then finally to seventh in line, and we thankfully never had any problems. Sasha had an ideal attitude, but each dog reacts differently. Yours might meet the baby, decide she doesn't want anything to do with him, and go about her business. Or your dog might instantly bond with your baby, and God help any person she doesn't know trying to pick up the baby. Your dog's reaction has a lot to do with her breed, age, and personality.

There are several methods to introduce your pet to your new baby. One of the most common is to bring in a blanket that your baby slept with at the hospital before you bring the baby into your home, to allow your dog to get a little familiar with his smell. This is a great exercise to do, even if you bring a blanket for your dog to smell right before your baby enters your home for the first time. At the end of the day, much comes down to positive reinforcement when you introduce your dog to your newest pack member, as well as during their interactions.

If you bring in a new member to the pack and are constantly shooing her away, your dog will be understandably upset. Let her meet your new baby, let her smell him, and this might be hard to hear, but yes, your dog will lick your new baby—and we all know where they were licking five minutes before. If you have a dog, you have to be okay with her licking the baby. Many studies do show that homes with pets provide children with better-developed immune systems and fewer allergies, because they are always bringing in fun, new germs from the outside.[19] So don't shoo your dog away. When your dog and baby first meet, give your dog some treats and let her associate the baby with treats and praise. Keep in mind that even if your dog has a great relationship with your baby, sometimes dogs accidentally hurt babies by stepping on them. When your dog is lying down in a ball and you plop the baby in the little nook to take some pictures, or when your baby starts to crawl around your dog, she is likely to step on your wee lad, so be careful.

Typically, reinforcing a positive association with your baby makes for a happy relationship. However, if you find that the dog is aggressive or you do not feel that the dog is safe, there is a tool you can use. This

---

19 Alice Park, "Study: Why Dogs and Cats Make Babies Healthier," *Time* Magazine Online, July 9, 2012, http://healthland.time.com/2012/07/09/study-why-dogs-and-cats-make-babies-healthier/.

tool was taught to me by my friend Steve, who reha-
bilitated abused dogs. What you do is lay your dog
down on her back, which is a submissive position for
her, and lie on top of her for at least thirty seconds to
a minute. Then, have the lady of the house lie on top
of your dog for the same amount of time. When your
partner gets up, hold your dog down on her back and
put your baby on top of your dog as well. What you
are doing is showing your dog who's at the top in the
pack hierarchy. Do that exercise a minimum of five to
ten times and your dog should get the idea of who's
literally on top in the pack.

Another tool to establish dominance is to put your
fist in your dog's mouth while she is on her back in a
submissive position. Please remember to be gentle and
caring if you try these techniques. They are not meant
to harm your dog in any way; they should be done
with care with the purpose of teaching and training
your pet about some new behavior rules, not to hurt
your pet in any way. If you find that these tools are not
enough to settle your dog and you do not feel safe, well
then, it's up to you and your partner to make the decision to get some professional training or have to make
the difficult decision to let your dog go or not. If you

feel your baby is really at risk, although it will not be easy, you will have to make that call. Your baby is your baby. I hope you never have to make that decision.

Cats bring different concerns. After connecting with hundreds of guys who have cats around their babies, their primary concern is that the cat will climb into the crib and sit on the baby's face, which they do like to do, and possibly suffocate your baby. To deal with that, there are netted domes that can cover your crib. We have a cat now, and if we had a cat when the kids were infants, you can bet your bottom dollar we would have had a net over the crib. And just like with dogs, positive reinforcement works as well. Treats when they are around the baby will make a positive connection between your cat and your home's new member.

When it comes to baby-proofing, the amount of proofing you do depends on your personal comfort and confidence level and how you want your home to feel. Baby-proofing can be lax or extreme. There are even companies you can pay to come to your home and tell you how and what you need to baby-proof. I am sure they do a great job, but if you don't want to hire a baby-proofing advisor, here is how to determine what you need to baby-proof your home.

First off, remember that *Babies* documentary? Your baby will adapt to your environment, but there are definitely some changes that can and should be made to your home with each stage of development to help you feel safer while your little poopsy cruises around.

When they first get home, they will not be moving anywhere, so you have a good couple of months to get ready. However, you can prepare for their exploration as soon as you want, especially if you are going back to work and just want to knock it out.

First of all, lock up any chemicals from under the sink or other low places that they could even remotely have the chance to get to. Move cleaning products and chemicals to a high shelf in a closet. Also, be sure to pack away any fancy floor vases or other delicate, decorative items that could easily get knocked over and broken. They will be crawling sooner than you know, and this is one surefire way to prevent a bad scene.

While your baby is brand new, he will be spending a lot of time in his crib, so let's talk about crib safety, starting with baby monitors. Baby monitors today can have more bells and whistles than a Mission Impossible gadget. You can get amazing monitors that will alert you to any movement that the baby makes, but be warned that it can make you a little bananas getting alerted to his every move. Michelle and I have a small house, so we felt confident that we would hear the baby cry. We did not use a monitor unless we would go out in the yard or elsewhere outside. Again, choosing a baby monitor ultimately comes down to your comfort level.

With the first baby's crib, usually you have bumpers and other fancy bells and whistles. But you will soon see that tying and untying all of those little ties after you wash the bumper and putting them back in place quickly becomes a real pain in the tush. We ended up keeping things simple in the crib—a sheet and a hanging mobile for the baby. Going simple can also help to prevent sudden infant death syndrome. Today, all of the powers that be recommend no bumpers and nothing in the crib at all, which is safer and makes life a little easier.

As for sleeping positions, the thought today is that the safest way for infants to sleep is on their back. It has a lot to do with the strength in their neck and their ability to move their head from side to side. We had Eliana and Jonah sleep on their backs until they could move their necks, but with Sarah we did not wait as long. She loved being on her belly and hated being on her back. She was our third baby, which meant we felt more comfortable. When swaddled, we would put her not fully on her belly, but at an angle on her side, similar to the Five S's. When Lila came around, she slept in the swing the first few nights. Then we used the side position for her, and she ended up on her belly a bit sooner than the others. For the record, the safest way for your baby to sleep according to the latest research is, in fact, on their back.

When it comes to where your baby sleeps, most experts agree having your baby in your room but not in your bed is the best scenario. They will be close, so you can monitor them and also have the convenience of close proximity for the many nighttime feedings.

Having your baby in bed with you comes with the increased risk of smothering your baby by accident. There are those that promote the benefits of having your baby in bed with you, which are mainly the ease of breastfeeding and being close enough to hear if your baby is having breathing issues or having a crisis.

Besides obvious safety issues, having your baby in bed with you will ultimately also interfere with the intimacy of your relationship. There are arguments that say having your baby in your bed all the time in no way interferes with intimacy. While not the root of a couple's intimacy issues, if present, having your baby as your third in your marital bed certainly will not help the cause, so it's definitely something to be aware of.

As we discussed several times, your baby is taking cues and learning from day one. If your baby learns that your bed is his bed, good luck putting him in his crib when you want him out. He will not be so willing to go. However, there is a solution to this situation that is a win-win. Enter the co-sleeper. Before you say no way, let me share with you that I originally said no way to a co-sleeper, because I wanted to prevent the baby from getting used to sleeping in the bed. Truth be told, I did not actually know what a co-sleeper was—I just didn't like the sound of it.

Turns out that a co-sleeper is awesome! It is essentially a half of a Pack 'n Play that is attached to your mattress with a strap to keep it close. This allows the baby to be right next to your bed, but not in it, which is amazing for nighttime feedings. If your partner is breastfeeding, she can roll over, grab your little dumpling, and roll the baby to in between you both. We kept diapers, wipes, and grocery bags in the co-sleeper pockets so that when we would change the baby, we could toss the diaper in the bag and then on the floor to be thrown out in the morning. Michelle would nurse the baby while lying down and half asleep. When the baby finished nursing, she would roll the baby back into the co-sleeper, and done! The co-sleeper is the best of both worlds: the ease of having your baby close for nighttime feedings and in case of an emergency, while at the same time letting you preserve your space as a couple and establishing a less traumatic transition when you move your baby to his own space when the time is right.

One thing to always be on the lookout for is when they start to roll. As soon as a few weeks, your baby will start moving more and more, so be careful not to take your hand off him when you change his diaper, and avoid leaving him even for a minute in the center of your bed—even if he's surrounded by pillows. As Michelle discovered, they can roll right over the pillows when they want to!

The real hazards come up when they start crawling, because they will be exploring and getting into everything to learn about their environment. Here is when you'll want to survey the scene through the eyes of your baby and a professional baby-proofer.

Get on your hands and knees and crawl around to see what they see. That is a great way to determine pointy edges and where to baby-proof. Instead of blindly buying every gimmicky baby-proofing thing for a million bucks, go over the house with your partner. Maybe every edge does not need to be covered in foam. Maybe the coffee table has some real sharp edges you need to cover, but not the bricks on the hearth of the fireplace.

Ask yourself what you want your place to feel like. What is your household, family view on your baby and safety? There can be a happy, safe, medium ground. For example, when the kids start to crawl and explore, they will be all over the kitchen cupboards. You decide if it's okay for them to be in there. You should know that they love playing with pots, pans, spoons, cups, and utensils. You might be okay with them getting into that Tupperware drawer.

Definitely be conscious of doorstops. You know, the springy ones with the little caps on the ends? They love putting those in their mouth like candies. Consider removing them and replace them with door stops that you put onto the hinges. When they crawl, everything will go in their mouth, so it is a time that choking could happen easily.

Another hazard to be conscious of is plugged-in cell phone chargers—they could get hold of a dangling cord, put the end in their mouth, and get a nice shock. The little receptacle covers that prevent babies from sticking things in the socket are great; just be careful when they are pulled out to vacuum, because they are also a choking hazard if your baby gets her hands on it.

With your first baby, there will not be many little things lying around like Barbie shoes and Lego pieces. However, pennies under the couch, a pen cap, etc.— those are good choking hazards. A tool used by the pros is a toilet-paper tube. If something can fit down there, then they can choke on it.

Your baby will be a bit top heavy as he grows, so be careful if you put him in the nook of the couch to sit up for a second, because he can easily topple over and onto the floor (yes, that happened to us). Also, be conscious of keeping the toilet seats down; there have been many tragic reports of children who topple into the toilet and drown! Terrible. I thought this was uncommon until I met a new dad-to-be in class, and his niece died this way. This is a good reason to start keeping the lid down! As they get a bit older and start toddling, baby door-handle locks come in handy. Your baby will want to escape as soon as he can reach the door handle. When we picked levers for our door hardware, we never realized that we were creating an easy escape route for the kids. Once when Eliana was three, we looked all over for her before we realized that she had pulled the lever and walked right out of the front door into the yard. We put lever locks on that day! That kind of activity really happens and sometimes does not end well. Please learn from our mistakes! I still get nervous around the stairs. A tumble down the steps is never good at any age! We didn't want to take the chance of the kids falling down the steps, so we put gates at the top and the bottom of our stairs.

Another topic we cover a lot in class is whether you should have everyone use antiseptic on their hands before they touch your baby. That can only be answered by you individually. If you feel more comfortable with people doing that, then do it! The hardest thing about this baby is coming up with your own playbook. Some people feel fine if guests wash their hands in the sink with soap and water, and others want more. What time of the year is it? Is it the winter and cold and flu season? Maybe you are more cautious if you have your baby at that time of the year. If you decide to go out to a restaurant with your baby, know that waiters and waitresses are often outgoing people and may want to touch your baby. If you do not want every person walking by to be all over your baby, get a booth and put your baby inside. During the first year, they are still developing their immunity, so a little caution never hurt anyone.

Dirt and germs are not always the enemy. It has been proven that playing in the dirt is beneficial, and again helps them to build their immunity. That is one benefit of bringing your kids to the playground your-self, because we dads have a tendency to let our kids get a little dirtier than our counterparts.

Let's talk about car seats. The key with car seats is getting them locked in as tightly as possible. These days, I'd be hard pressed to believe that there are any cars that don't have latches to secure car seats. You can always use the seat belt to lock it in; however, using the latches to tether your car seat is night-and-day differ-ent. The latches are awesome and make it easier to get a really tight fit.

The first tip is more for the safety of your vehicle. Your car is going to get a bit gross because kids are gen-erally kind of gross, especially babies. You will have spit-up and boogers all over your car, so it helps to put a towel down under the car seat. You can also buy one of those plastic mats for underneath the car seat.

When your baby is little, the seat will be rear facing. In this configuration, you will get a little front-to-back wiggling since the back is not supported. Put your car seat in and hook one side of the latch to the hook that's in the crease between seats. Dig your knee into the seat, latch the other hook, and as you dig your knee into the seat as tightly as you can, pull the strap that tightens the seat to the car. The key is that you don't want any side-to-side play. Some say that the safest place for the infant seat is behind the front passenger seat as opposed to the center of the back seat, because many sedans have an armrest that comes out of the back-center part of the seat, which renders the center of the back seat hollow. This offers less support in an impact. That being said, you're going to end up putting it where it's most convenient for you. Michelle and I ended up putting the baby in the middle of the car. That's because if a side impact were to occur, we believed it would be better if the baby were in the center of the car.

After a while, we ended up putting the car seats behind the driver side for the sake of ease. You put the baby in and then jump in the front seat. Whichever spot you decide, the key is to dig in your knee and get the seat as tight as possible. There are still some fire departments and baby stores that have "certified" car-seat installers that can check your work if you would feel safer about your installation. Not all fire departments provide this service, so call first.

God forbid, but in case you are in a car accident, one good Hero Tool is to keep an index card in the back of the baby's seat with his name, your contact info, and his blood type. This ensures that even if you are rendered unconscious in the case of an accident, emergency responders have your baby's information right there in the car seat.

Your next Hero Tool is to remember that you are going to have to be consistent with your messages. It will simply not be enough to tell little Sally not to go out the front door five times. She will need to hear it five hundred times, especially if she is a real explorer. This can become really frustrating, and the lesson here is that they just don't get it yet.

WE WANT TO BELIEVE THAT THEY DO BECAUSE WE TOLD THEM A ZILLION TIMES NOT TO DO WHATEVER, BUT HONESTLY, THEY DON'T GET IT AND CANNOT GET IT UNTIL THEY GET OLDER. UNDERSTANDING THAT WISDOM MAY HELP YOU AVOID GIVING THEM A SPANKING OR WORSE IF YOU REMEMBER THIS WHEN YOU FEEL FRUSTRATED THAT IT'S HAPPENING AGAIN. THEY JUST DON'T GET IT, AND IT IS NOT THEIR FAULT THEY DON'T GET IT. THEY ARE JUST NOT THERE YET.

Patience is huge. I am not saying it is easy—I have lost it more times than I can count. To improve as a parent, I work on this all of the time. The goal is to not lose my cool more than I already do, and that happens when I remember to first take three to five deep breaths and then tell myself, "It is not their fault; they don't get it yet." Sometimes, my friend, it seems they will never get it. You just have to hang in there and stay consistent with your messages!

The next topic I'd like to talk about comes into play when your baby gets a bit older, and it's a touchy one:

firearms. No matter your opinion on firearms, it's a reality that some families do have them in their home. There are many homes that have firearms in the United States that are very safe and never have issues. At the core, a firearm is a tool, just like a drill, blender, pencil, or fork is a tool, each with a specific purpose and all of which can hurt you if you don't know what you're doing. I grew up in a home with firearms, and we never had any issues. Here are the tools I attribute to that experience: age-appropriate introduction, consistent safety education, and reinforcement. It also helped that the firearms were not a taboo subject. Just like sex and drugs, my parents discussed these tough topics to educate us before we were influenced out of the home, and it paid off.

As with most sensitive topics that come up, you may be thinking the good question of when you should discuss hard topics like where babies come from or, in this case, what is in that metal box. Michelle and I tend to address these questions when our kids ask. They are thinking about the topic already, and if they do not get an answer, you can be sure they will be asking someone else until they do. My older kids were seven and six when they first asked what was in the metal box, and

I used it as an opportunity to educate them. I opened it up and explained that there was a gun in the box. I explained that it was not like in a TV show—they can hurt you and kill you (even though they did not truly get the concept, it was good for them to hear so they would understand it the more we reinforced it). I told them that they could touch it only if they asked, and that the number-one rule when it comes to firearms is that a gun is always loaded. That was the first rule my dad taught me about guns, and it's the same rule my children will tell you. Accidents happen when people assume a gun is unloaded, and the consequences are irreversible. A gun is never safe.

I teach my kids safety, safety, safety. They know that we have guns in the house, so we eliminate the taboo factor. I know that if we try to hide our guns, they *will* find them, so we don't make it a secret. They have seen them and held them, and if they want to see them, I will show them. That way they never need to feel as if they are totally inaccessible, which would only make them want them more. They also are taught that it is a family secret and never to be discussed with their friends, because everyone has different views and we want to be respectful of them. We've also shared and reinforced that if they go to someone's house and there is an unsupervised firearm, leave the house and come home if it is within walking distance. If not, they should call me right away.

Education is the key, but there are also responsibilities on your end as a parent. The firearms should always be locked up so your kids are never in a position to be able to touch a firearm unsupervised.

The next tool is an "In Case of Emergency" Phone Number Worksheet, which you can print from the Hero Dad website. All you need to do is fill in your information and put it somewhere easy to get to. We have ours taped up inside our kitchen-cabinet door. This way if you go out for the evening and you have a babysitter, they have all of your important information in one spot. Your go-to numbers will be on the sheet, such as your home address and home phone number; your cell numbers; poison control; your pediatrician's, vet's, parents', and neighbors' numbers; and other numbers. You should also have a how-to sheet in case of choking, just like you would find in a restaurant, which you can also download from www.TheHero-Dad.com.

A good first-aid kit is always nice to have in the home, as well as your car and diaper bags. After twelve years and four kids worth of boo-boos, the most-used first-aid items for us have been Band-Aids and boo-boo packs, which is what we call our ice packs. We use a variety of Band-Aid sizes and reusable, flexible ice packs that can wrap around an arm, elbow, or knee. The ice packs that come in a soft outer shell with Velcro straps are really great.

When you hit the playground, carry in your dad diaper bag the kind of ice packs that turn cold when you crush them. Depending on your ability and desire to do first aid, you can create a really extensive first-aid kit, but if you don't have much training, you can simply keep swelling down with an ice pack and control minor cuts and scrapes with Band-Aids. With those tools, you should be able to handle most playground injuries. Remember the old saying "With bigger kids come bigger problems," or, in this case, bigger injuries. As they get bigger, Neosporin or the like with pain relief, children's Tylenol, an antihistamine, topical bug-bite stuff, and calamine lotion are all good tools for your kit. Having a copy of your emergency contact numbers is also a great tool for your first-aid kit.

The next tools fall into home and family safety rather than being child specific. You might love them, or you might think they are a little over the top. However, it is better to have a tool and not need it than to need a tool and not have it. A Hero Dad is prepared, so one of my favorites is a car-emergency-escape keychain. In the event that you are trapped inside a car after an accident, pull the tool off your keychain, slice your seat belt off if it is jammed, and then simply push the device against the car window. It has a spring-loaded metal piece that pops out to shatter the glass so that you can escape. It may seem overboard, but these things happen. When I was twelve, my mom rolled our Suburban on the way to visit my brother at camp. After the accident, the frame was smashed, and we had to punch out the windshield to get out. I remember hating the idea we were trapped. A car-escape keychain makes light work of exiting a vehicle in an emergency with your family. They are small and unassuming, yet they get the job done. If you have never seen one, check them out on the Hero Dad website.

The next tool could be a lifesaver, and it is that you and your wife may want to consider leaving the headphones home next time you go for a jog with the baby. The rate of distracted drivers is ever increasing, putting pedestrians at risk.[20] Being aware of your surroundings, especially when crossing streets and intersections, could save your life by giving you an extra second to react to a driver who is preoccupied and may not see you and your stroller.

This next tool for your consideration is a water-filtration system for your home. It is very popular to have a filter on your sink; however, we bathe and wash our food in the water that is not filtered. Depending on where you live, it may be beneficial to have some extra filtration. You and I both know that we cannot protect ourselves from everything, but water is important to our survival at a basic level, and our municipality's water-filtration systems simply cannot catch every little

---

20 Lecia Bushak, "Distracted Drivers Cause Pedestrian Deaths To Rise 50% From Texting, Talking On Phone, Or Eating At The Wheel," Medical Daily, November 30, 2013, http://www.medicaldaily.com/distracted-drivers-cause-pedestrian-deaths-rise-50-texting-talking-phone-or-eating-wheel-264077.

particulate today in your water that could potentially be harmful to you and your family. It doesn't hurt to have the cleanest water you can going onto and into your family. The last home-safety tool for you to consider is a whole-home, natural gas–operated generator that turns on automatically in the case of a real power outage. Imagine you are on a business trip and a storm rolls in and wipes out the power. When the power goes out, your generator kicks in, and your family is not left in the dark. Imagine what a hero you will be!

My friend, hopefully you're feeling a little bit more confident about what you can do to keep your family safe. Remember, no one is expecting you to be an EMT—just to be cool enough to figure out your next safety move as quickly as possible. In the end, just do the best you can to keep your kids safe. However, you cannot watch them every second, and their freedom to play and explore is priceless. Although you cannot control the bumps and bruises they'll get along the way, you can control your reaction and response if and when an accident happens.

CHAPTER 8

BONDING

JUST as it is important to come closer with your partner during this transition into a family, it is also important (and enjoyable!) to invest time into bonding with your baby. When thinking about the process of bonding and your budding relationship with your newborn, it is important to remember how a relationship is developed.

ANY RELATIONSHIP THAT YOU HAVE IN YOUR LIFE WAS DEVELOPED, HOW? THROUGH TIME AND EXPERIENCES SHARED.

The reason why this is important to remember is that there is not always an immediate bond or connection that happens with your baby. Personally, bonding did not happen for me and Eliana for, dare I say, two and half or three months. I remember feeling really crappy after being more than two months into fathering and not feeling significantly more attached to our baby. I was involved—feeding the baby, changing the baby, rocking the baby—and even still, I had no heartstring connection to her. I felt awful about it.

After speaking to some other fathers who were a bit ahead of me in the process, it turned out I was not alone. It's relatively common, because even though you are doing a good job and you're involved, most of the baby's waking hours are spent initially with his mom, especially if after a week you are back to work, and your baby is being breastfed.

You may get lucky and bond right away, or you may not. However, if you fall into the nonimmediate-bonding group as I did, the important fact to remember is that all you need to do is give it some more time and stay the course. Stay involved, keep spending time with your baby, and you will wake up one day feeling closely connected. I went from feeling completely disconnected to perhaps overboard, if that is possible. These days, I probably spend too much time thinking about tortures that I would do to any person who would touch my children inappropriately! Just you wait and see. Your innate desire to protect your cubs will amaze you. Once you bond, you will never have a stronger connection to anyone except your partner, who is the only other person in the world who is going through the exact things you are.

When we talk about bonding with our children, there is another topic we should talk about, and that is your expectations. For example, if you were hoping for a daughter and find out you will have a son or vice versa, you may find yourself holding back from bonding because you are disappointed. We all have our own reasons for what we want our first baby to be. I wanted a son first. I grew up in a home with two older brothers and wanted a boy! I dreamed of doing boy stuff with him, but we ended up having a girl first. Finding out our first was a girl did leave me a bit deflated, although I knew we were planning on having more kids. I did get my boy, Jonah, who came second. When number three turned out to be another girl, Sarah, I thought for sure that when we got pregnant with number four, it would be a boy. We hoped that the family would "balance out," giving us two and two. However, it didn't happen that way; we got ourselves another girl, Lila.

When the ultrasound tech said it was a girl, I was definitely sad. I really had grown attached to the idea of having another boy, and it was disappointing for me. I was disappointed for my son, because now our girl had a girl, but Jonah would not have a little brother. Michelle did not have to ask if I was sad; it was clear. When I expressed I was disappointed to Michelle, was she understanding? Not really! She told me to get over it.

I understand if you are disappointed, so consider this: If you are disappointed, it is okay to be disappointed! Michelle eventually came around and understood. I knew that it was better that I expressed my feelings, because it enabled me to move past them. To pretend that you are not upset, to not give yourself that permission to be disappointed, would be much worse. Ignoring negative feelings will increase the odds that those feelings will show up and have a negative effect during your bonding process.

If you are blessed with a healthy child, in the big picture you are very lucky indeed. If you have a girl or boy, I promise you, you will love them and you will have fun with them. And it may turn out differently than you think! A good friend of mine has a daughter who knows every single player on the Braves, their stats, and what positions they play. Your child will want to spend time with you doing whatever it is you like to do, boy or girl.

If you did really want the boy first, you will come to terms with having a girl eventually. When you do, peruse the book *Strong Fathers, Strong Daughters* by Dr. Meg Meeker. The statistics of how important our influence is on our daughters really will blow your mind. Boys need us as a strong role model to learn how to be a good man. However, our daughters need us just as much to learn how a woman should be treated. If they don't have a healthy relationship with Dad, the odds will increase that they will look for love in the wrong places later in life.

In the end, there is nothing I would trade my youngest daughter, Lila, for. Please take that the ultimate blessing is to have a healthy child, and that if you do not get what you think you wanted at first, it is okay to feel those feelings. It will only help you to accept, love, and bond with your baby more quickly. And don't lose sight that you can always try again, and again, and again.

CHAPTER 9

WHAT A HERO DAD KNOWS ABOUT STUFF

THE next topic we are going to cover is stuff. That's right—baby gadgets and accessories. One of the most common questions I get when teaching my dad class is, what kind of stuff is actually necessary? Many times, men share that their house is becoming a warehouse full of baby contraptions. So, what kind of stuff do you really need? What's important to have if you're on a budget? What stuff can you return?

We have a saying in our house that the best things in life aren't really things. At the end of the day, the only things that you truly need when you're introducing a new baby into your home are food, diapers, shelter, and of course, a lot of patience.

Today, there are many things and gadgets that make life easier when introducing the baby into your home and raising the baby through the infant phase. I will share with you the top five items that helped us through the baby and infant stages of four children—items that not only helped us, but also stood the test of time.

On the top of the list would for sure be a comfortable glider or rocking chair, because you're going to be spending a lot of time in that chair. You'll be nursing the baby, bonding with the baby, hanging out with the baby, getting to know your baby, and rocking your baby to sleep. We have a glider, and to this day, it is one of our favorite pieces of furniture—fourteen years after our first baby was born! It's one of the most coveted seats in our house. I can't say enough of the importance of having a comfortable chair.

Because I teach the new-dads class, I'm always looking at different baby furniture and gadgets. It's amazing to see that some of the gliders have a low back. Not everybody is extremely tall, but I'm surprised that they would make any glider meant for the baby phase with a low back. So many times when you're in that chair, you're going to be tired, which means you will rest your head back. You might even nod off while you are feeding your baby in the middle of the night. You want to have something to support the back of your neck so that you don't lay your head all the way back and hit it on the chair frame. So, when you're shopping for a chair, keep the height of the back in mind.

We have a Dutailier glider. I want to plug them here because the only thing we've ever had to change on that chair is the cushions. It is very well made, and we've never had a problem with it. There are a zillion chair makers, so do your research and find one that has good reviews and that is comfortable. If you had to spend a few extra dollars, something to get is a better-quality glider. It is worth it because of the amazing amount of time you will spend in the chair.

Now that you have your chair, number two on the list is a swaying or a bouncy chair for your baby. You will want to have a vessel that you can put your baby into that moves or that you can rock. Remember that one of the Five S's is Sway; they love the movement. Just like the glider or the rocking chair, a bouncy chair or swing is a great soothing tool to have for your new baby. It's also nice to have something that you can put the baby in to give you a break between feedings. Our number-four baby, Lila, spent her first two nights at home in the swing. In between feedings, we swaddled her up and strapped her in. At night, we put her in the swing next to the bed and she loved it. The swing is a good babysitter because the babies are contained and soothed. One dad told me that his baby didn't really like the swing but loved the bouncy chair. If it's not one, it will be the other—chances are, your baby will like some kind of apparatus that will bounce, move, shake, or vibrate.

Number three is a Pack 'n Play, which is great for so many reasons. First, it's another place for the baby to hang out and sleep in that is away from its primary sleeping area. This is beneficial because when you create an environment for the baby that they're comfortable with, you're able to travel more. When it's time to go to your buddy's to watch the game or to your in-laws', just bring the Pack 'n Play, and your baby will have a safe, familiar place where they can play and nap.

Number four is a baby carrier. Whether you're out and about or at home doing chores, you want to have something that frees your hands while you carry your baby. The key is getting something that's comfortable. We've tried many different baby carriers, and the one we liked best was the Ergobaby. Most carriers have one function where you can either carry your baby in the front or on your back. The Ergobaby, however, is convertible. You can use it to carry your baby on the front, back, or side—one baby carrier that does it all. It has thick straps for the shoulders and around your waist, and any dad would be comfortable in it whether you are a small-framed or extra-large-framed dad. We did have a different carrier for when we were hiking and backpacking, a heavy-duty pack that had a metal frame on it. But for everyday purposes, the Ergobaby is fantastic.

Rounding out number five would be a copy of *The Happiest Baby on the Block*. God bless that Dr. Karp. He really created a set of life-changing tools. He helped cut the curve of learning how to soothe your baby, and I'd be remiss not to include it. A copy of *The Happiest Baby on the Block* is great to have in the house as a reference, and you can always go back and rewatch if you have another baby and need a refresher.

These are the top five gadgets or "tools" that have proven over and over again to be valuable and needed resources when it comes to the new babies. Are there other tools that are absolutely fantastic? Of course there are. To name a few, one would be a bottle sterilizer. You can clean the bottle so quickly without having to put it in the dishwasher or wash it by hand. Throw it in the machine, hit the button, and it will sterilize the bottles, nipples, and other parts and pieces. Our friends love their sterilizers. A good baby monitor is always nice to have as well so you can be outside around the house and still have an eye or ear on your baby. The list of good stuff could go on and on.

The thing about the baby stuff is that you can spend a small fortune on all of these different tools. However, there are ways to save a ton of money on baby stuff. Consignment shops, secondhand stores, Goodwill, and garage sales are great resources to save a lot of your hard-earned dollars.

The reason it's so smart to get secondhand baby stuff is that it's practically brand new. Much of the baby stuff you will find at these stores hasn't gotten much use because babies develop so rapidly. Babies go through developmental changes every couple of months and quickly grow out of and lose interest in the stuff that they loved just the other day. Due to rapid developmental changes, you can get stuff for smaller babies in especially nice condition, sometimes with the tags still on. Plus, people get doubles of gifts and then give them away. As your baby gets into the toddler phase, the stuff takes a bit of a beating, which is another reason to save money on clothes.

We use Goodwill and find it to be a fantastic resource. I don't think I've been to Goodwill without seeing at least one brand-new Pack 'n Play in the box. Not every area has a Goodwill, but almost every area has consignment shops and garage sales.

However, many people have mixed emotions about buying secondhand. Many men express that they would like to save the money, but their partners take issue with getting secondhand clothes. Everybody has different comfort levels when it comes to this topic. If you happen to fall into the camp of people who know that babies indeed change and will grow out of and sometimes destroy their toys and clothes, then this tool can work for you. At the end of the day, children really don't know the difference, and you can save a tremendous amount of money.

HAVING A NEW BABY IS ALREADY STRESSFUL FOR NEW PARENTS, AND MONEY IS ONE OF THE TOP REASONS COUPLES FIGHT. IF YOU TWO COULD SAVE SOME MONEY AND YOUR BABY WON'T KNOW THE DIFFERENCE, WHY NOT SAVE WHERE YOU CAN? USING SECONDHAND STORES IS A TOOL, NOT A RULE.

If you can find a brand-new Pack 'n Play that can go to Grandma's house without paying a premium, then that is a win, no matter how much money you have in the bank. You'll benefit from some extra money to take care of business, pay the bills, or have a well-deserved night out.

You'd be surprised to know that the kids love the secondhand stores. At how many stores can you tell your kids, "Pick anything you want"?

Next, here is an amazing tool to help you manage all of the stuff, because you're going to accumulate a lot of it. As mentioned, each phase in your baby's development will come with its own toys, tools, and contraptions. To manage the clutter, consider the Black-Bag Operation. When your kid is at Grandma's house or daycare or preschool, go into the toy area with a black garbage bag. Keep his favorite stuff that he is currently into, and clean out the rest. This might sound pretty awful, but it's fantastic! The stuff will be gone and your little angel will not even notice that anything is missing. You can do a Black-Bag Operation anytime you start to feel like the clutter is building up. You can even save a couple of old, favorite toys and reintroduce them at a later date, and your kid will love them again.

To help set your expectations, you should know that your children will help you to be less materialistic, mostly because they will break and vandalize your possessions! Work on developing your sense of humor and patience. Sooner than you imagine, your little angel who was just born will be the same kid who Sharpies on your walls, leaves rotting milk in countless sippy cups under the couch, clogs your toilets, breaks every pair of glasses you own, and throws the remote into your TV screen "by accident" (but not before wiping boogers on the screen). A good friend of mine's kid threw his Wii remote right through his new sixty-inch TV screen. Oops, sorry! No matter how loud you yell, your child has no clue how hard you work for the nice things in your home.

If you can accept that is what happens when you have kids, no matter how clean and tidy you and your partner keep your house, you will save yourself many headaches.

KNOW THAT YOU WILL NEED A SHEETROCK AND PAINT TOUCH-UP IN THREE TO FOUR YEARS. WORK ON KEEPING A HEALTHY SENSE OF HUMOR ABOUT IT ALL, AND KNOW THAT THIS TOO SHALL PASS. REMEMBER THAT WHEN IT COMES TO STUFF AND THINGS, THE BEST THINGS IN LIFE REALLY AREN'T THINGS.

CHAPTER 10

TRAVELING

THE next topic is one that always comes up in class, and that is traveling with your new baby. "Is it okay to travel? Should we travel? My dad traveled all the time and it sucked for me as a kid, but wouldn't you know it, I have a job that requires me to travel. What should I do?"

If you like to travel, you should travel! Do it! Traveling with an infant is really easy compared to when your infant becomes a toddler. A toddler is more of a challenge to travel with because they don't want to sit still. Your small baby is easy to travel with by plane or car because they are tied into a car seat and can't go anywhere! Besides schlepping the gear, which is the hardest part, traveling with a baby is relatively easy. There is no rule to what age your baby needs to be before traveling. It just depends on your comfort level. Your baby's immune system will not be 100 percent for about a year, so that is something to take into consideration. However, if you have a healthy baby, then traveling through an airport should not be an issue. Figuring out how to change the baby in that tiny airplane bathroom is another story.

My family lives in New York, and since we like to see them, we have driven and flown several times. Today, my kids are eight, ten, twelve, and fourteen, and they go through security at the airport like champs. Because they have done it so many times, they know the drill and move right through. There are guys I know who are unwilling to travel by air because it seems like a big deal, but just like anything else, if you make it a big deal, it will be. If you are cool about it, your kids will be too and will follow your lead.

When going through security and traveling in general, remember this rule about taking your baby: Everything takes twice as long and you get half as much done. If you are flying, time is your Hero Tool! Make sure you plan enough time to get through all of the hoops. If you can bring an umbrella stroller that folds up small, that helps, but it is not always possible. Using your baby carrier frees up your hands to carry luggage. Pack as light as you can. Security usually is gracious when it comes to helping parents with young kids get through. If you can secure a car seat at your destination, that will also make your life and traveling experience much easier.

Another tool is to be conscious of food in case your flight is delayed. If your partner is breastfeeding, you should be good to go. If not, make sure you have enough formula to carry you through a flight delay, because last I checked, they do not sell breast milk or formula at the newspaper stands!

Definitely take advantage of boarding early when they make the announcements for families with small children so you can get in there and get situated. And until they are around three years old, you do not need to pay for a seat for your baby, which is nice. When you get settled in, be prepared to deal with your baby's ears popping by feeding her during takeoff and landing. When she is sucking and moving her jaw, it helps to keep her ears clear and avoid discomfort from the changes in air pressure.

Changing your baby is always fun in the airplane bathroom, though I would often use my changing pad. I'd bring the baby in the back by the attendant station and change her super quick right there on the floor! Your Airplane Changing Tool is to have gallon-size zip-lock bags with you to store your baby's stinkaroo diapers so they do not stink up the airplane! Works like a charm. Remember to let the air out before you seal the bag, because if you don't and the bag gets inadvertently squeezed and pops, you will have a stink bomb on your hands. Yes, it has happened to me, and it's really embarrassing.

If you plan plenty of time, flying with your baby is a piece of cake. As they get older, traveling and keeping them in their seats does get more challenging; however, you have a little while until that happens.

As they get older, it is all about having activities planned, and these days with mobile devices and movies, it is easier than ever to keep them entertained. One time we were flying home from New York carrying sandwiches from my mom's house with food for the flight. Eliana dared Jonah to eat the Styrofoam cup that his drink came in. He won the bet and then proceeded to puke his sandwich and cup all over the place! We can laugh about it now, but the point is to enjoy traveling when they are small!

Traveling by car is easy in that there are not usually many pressure changes in the cabin, and you have all of your gear at your disposal. You can stop when you need to change your little traveler in training. Again, it is important to plan extra time for the pit stops.

With traveling for work, in the end, you have to do what you have to do. If you have any influence over the traveling, then make some changes to avoid the same experience you may have had as a kid if your father traveled often for work. If your job simply requires you to travel, then do the best you can to spend as much time as possible with them when you are home, or you always could consider making a job change. Keep in mind that just because you travel for work, all is not lost. Much of the success behind being a Hero Dad comes from the quality of the time you spend with your baby and children when you are together.

Because being away from your wife and new baby is stressful, it might be easy to forget that your partner is having a stressful time at home with the baby as well. If you remember that, it could help you to avoid the "What do you mean you had a stressful trip? You were away and I was taking care of the baby!" argument.

Ultimately, if you want to do things differently and create your idea of a great childhood for your kid, you can. You can create the family life you have dreamed about. Doing that just takes effort, changes to our hardwiring (sometimes), and a bit of out-of-the-box thinking and decision making to make it happen. Think more about what is best for you and your family, and less about what is the "norm."

CHAPTER 11

SEX AND RELATIONSHIPS

IF you are a human male, then keeping sex in your life is an important topic to discuss. As men, it is in our nature to want sex, and when we are not having it, we are typically thinking about it. When you are married, what better place to get it than your own home?

Only you know what your sex drive is and how much or how little you need to feel fulfilled sexually and intimately. Hopefully, you and your partner have a healthy enough relationship that you can share what you need with your partner and she feels safe enough to share what she needs with you. Whatever that amount is, it is important to your relationship that you both feel fulfilled in this department, or the odds will increase that you will have conflict.

My brother Jason once told me that sex is like money—it is only a problem when you do not have it. My friend, you are about to not have it for at least three to six weeks because your partner needs to heal from the birth.

Sex with your partner after having a baby is considerably better for several reasons, which we will get into. It's getting started again that is typically the challenge. What you are about to learn is a proven plan and strategy, with tools to increase your odds at a smooth transition back into Booty Town, no disrespect for your partner intended!

THE PLAN IS BROKEN DOWN INTO THREE PHASES, WITH TOOLS IN EACH PHASE THAT BUILD ON ONE ANOTHER. THE FIRST PHASE IS FROM BIRTH TO WHEN YOUR PARTNER IS HEALED. THE SECOND PHASE OF THE PLAN IS FROM HER BEING HEALED TO WHEN YOUR BABY IS SLEEPING THROUGH THE NIGHT, AND THE FINAL PHASE IS FOR AFTER YOUR BABY FINDS HER WAY OUT OF YOUR ROOM AND INTO HER OWN.

I like to call Phase One the Selfless Phase. After the baby is born, there is certain amount of time for your wife to heal before you can physically have sex with her again, and that time frame is typically three to six weeks. Every woman will heal differently, but the real answer to when sex will start again has less to do with healing and more to do with when your wife says she's feeling ready again.

THE KEY HERE IS WHEN SHE IS FEELING READY.

For the most part, sex will now have a lot more to do with feelings. There are definitely, hopefully, nights of hot passion, although even those have a lot to do with—dare I say it?—feelings of connection and trust.

With helping your partner to feel ready again, you can start by actively trying many of the tools you have already been learning. Being involved from the start, massaging, and communicating will all have her trusting you more and feeling more in love with you, which is a great place to start.

The next tool for you is pure gold: knowing your partner's love language and her knowing yours. By knowing your partner's love language, your efforts toward making your wife happy will be infinitely more effective! Here, you and I must give thanks to Gary Chapman, who is the author of *The 5 Love Lan-*

guages. Like Dr. Karp, he created tools to help us in the love and romance department.

This is the main idea. We all give and receive love in different ways. Chapman breaks it down to five ways, or love languages. They are gifts given, quality time, words of praise, acts of service, and physical touch. We typically have two main languages that really speak to us. You might associate giving a gift with showing how much you love your partner. You may give words of praise: "Honey, great job with caring for the baby," or "Wow, you look really pretty." You may pick up the dry cleaning and help with the laundry to show you care, which are acts of service. You may lovingly hug your partner, which is touch, or sit with your partner and watch a show, which is considered quality time.

Problems occur when you show love by giving little gifts all the time, but your partner recognizes love by words of praise. You can be making an effort and showing you love her in *your* language of love, but it won't translate to her if she speaks a different language. She perceives that you love her when you share with her that she looks pretty or other words of praise, as opposed to receiving a gift or other token of affection.

You can see how you can absolutely love your partner and be making an effort, yet have it all go to waste if none of your effort registers to your partner as love. This happened to Michelle and me, because she prefers quality time and acts of service, whereas I am more likely to give physical touch and words of praise. For a long time, I did not think she loved me or really "got" me. She was always giving me acts of service like entering the bills instead of sitting on my lap and telling me she loves me, which speaks to me more strongly.

I had to wrap my mind around the concept of the languages, because I realized it was on target and true. Growing up, Michelle did not have such a touchy-feely home, so it was not what she was used to but still was what I needed, and vice versa. Meanwhile, I would hug Michelle and tell her that I loved her, which didn't register with her. Once we understood what each other's love languages were, the energy we spent became much more effective.

GETTING INVOLVED AND UNDERSTANDING HER LOVE LANGUAGE WILL PUT YOU MILES AHEAD OF YOUR NEIGHBOR, WHO IS SPENDING HIS LOVING-ENERGY CURRENCY IN THE WRONG DEPARTMENT, WHICH IS A MAJOR MISTAKE IN THIS CRUCIAL, VERY EMOTIONAL, TRANSITIONAL TIME FOR YOU BOTH.

Plus, there is another serious benefit for you. There comes a time in a marriage when your wife's role shifts from being her parents' daughter first to your wife first and their daughter second. Much of the switch has to do with proving yourself as a man who will take care of her. Depending on how long you have been with your wife, this shift could have happened already. If not, having a baby together is a real opportunity to earn that switch. She needs to trust in you 100 percent and know that you will be there to help her and be her partner through this crazy parenting experience. There is another level to your relationship now. You are more than just partners or husband and wife; you are also a mother and father with a child in your life.

Bringing your baby home could definitely bring your relationship to a new level, which has the ability to translate into the bedroom as well.

We covered the benefits of using a co-sleeper in the safety chapter; these benefits will also translate into your intimacy. Will your baby end up in your bed with you in the course of her infancy? Of course she will. Letting your baby sleep with you every once in a while, or when she is sick, is different from moving her to your bed full time.

As we discussed several times, your baby is taking cues and learning from day one. If your baby learns that your bed is her bed, good luck putting her in her crib when you want her out. She will not be so willing to go.

Having a "family bed" definitely sounds romantic and truly does work for some couples. You may know one. When you talk to them at parties, they say everything is awesome. The two men that I have known personally who said they loved the family bed are both divorced now.

Food for thought: your child will not always be an infant. Think about tomorrow and the next phase after infancy and how nice it will be to have some space to stretch out and relax in after working so hard all day, every day with your partner to raise your baby. There is something to be said for having a special place as parents, and your bedroom can be that place.

The last tool in the first Selfless Phase that will hold you over and keep you sane, you learned in junior high school. Thankfully, it works the same now.

When your partner gets the okay from her doctor and is feeling open and connected to you, Phase Two will begin. Your first tool in Phase Two is the quickie.

EMBRACE THE QUICKIE.

A quickie is great for your wife because she will still be exhausted. A quickie will not take much of her energy, other than her willingness to let you make it happen. If you have been hooking her up by being an involved and loving partner, she might be ready to hook you up in return. The baby could be down for a nap and it is quiet, or maybe your mother-in-law is watching the baby. Bring it up. Ask your partner if you can talk to her for a minute upstairs and make it happen. Just make sure you let her know that when she is ready, you will take the time to give her what she needs when she needs it.

TOOL NUMBER TWO IS TO CATCH YOUR WOMAN IN THE SHOWER.

You know that expression "I wash your back, you wash mine"? Take it literally. When you have children, the shower is a great place for sex and to connect in general. You will both already be naked and clean, and you can both get cleaned up afterward, all in one. Showering is something you have to do anyway, and finding the time to be alone and connect is often the roadblock to being intimate.

A tool that can make showering together a habit is to add a second shower head so that you do not freeze your butt off, which is the main problem with showering together. Easy to fix. If you ever redo your shower, just have the plumber add a second shower head. If that's not in the cards, there are attachments you can get today at your local hardware store that can turn a single shower head into a double. You can make it happen even if you are not handy.

Phase Three will begin after your baby starts sleeping through the night. Let's talk for a minute about when to move your baby to her own room. Aside from intimacy concerns, this is an important topic to discuss, and it comes up in my classes all the time.

When you have children in your room, it is ultimately more difficult to be romantic, connect, and have sex with your wife, which is one of the perks of being married. For that reason, it is okay to discuss when the baby could go to her room. A good time to work on that transition is when she starts sleeping through the night, which usually happens around three months if you are working on spreading out her feedings per a systematic approach like the one in *Baby Wise*.

There is no right or wrong here. Some couples decide to keep their baby in their room for up to a year. One pregnant woman I was chatting with one day shared with me that she and her husband had two other kids at home and they were both still sleeping in their room. When I asked her if she and her husband ever have the opportunity to be intimate, she just looked at me and asked what I meant. I said, "When do you two have the opportunity to be intimate and connect alone, without your children in your room?" She replied, "Not so much." I have to admit, I felt bad for her husband. Any way you slice it, from a husband-and-wife perspective, it will be healthier for your marriage to get the kids out and have a special space for you and your partner to connect as a couple. Ultimately, your family will be as strong as your marriage, and being intimate and connected emotionally and physically with your partner as often as possible is one of the best ways for that to happen.

Transitioning your first out of your room is difficult, because it breaks your heart when she is crying and you're used to rushing in to soothe her. When you are transitioning a baby who can sleep through the night, try the Five-Minute-Increment Tool. After we put Eliana in her own room for the night, if she woke up crying, we would hold out for five minutes to see if she would fall back asleep. If she did not, one of us would soothe her. The next night, we would hold off for ten minutes. Eventually, she would realize we were not coming to get her and go back to sleep.

We also used this Five-Minute-Increment Tool when we were lengthening the time between feedings.

You and your lady will decide when it is right for you to move your baby out. Once your baby is out, you will both sleep more soundly and get more rest, which changes everything. Your life will be back to your new normal. More rest also means more capacity for intimacy.

Furthermore, when your baby is out, get out the baby paraphernalia! It may sound crazy, and that might be because the idea came from a fêng shui book. However, if your home is not already littered with baby stuff, it will be. Talk to your wife about keeping all of the baby stuff out and the couple stuff in. For example, we only have pictures of Michelle and me in our bedroom. We keep pictures from when we started dating and pictures of us having fun together, and the reason is to have a constant reminder of us as a couple. Will their stuff migrate to your room? Yes, of course. Try to get it out on a regular basis.

Another tool is to batten down the hatches. Install a bolt lock on the inside of your door! That is right—a bolt lock. The little handle lock has failed on us too many times as the kids were hammering and banging on the door, which yours will be doing sooner than you think. Having a good lock will help you and your wife to feel safe to do what you have to without the feeling that someone will be bursting through the door and you will have to explain why you were playing horsey with Mommy. You can wait until your baby is a little older to install your lock. However, you will blink and your child will be knocking at your door!

Our door is only closed if we are connecting after work or if we are having some Mommy and Daddy time. Otherwise, it is always open. When it is closed, the kids are relentless, and having that extra lock sets our minds at ease that the door will stay locked.

You should also create a phrase for your connecting time and get it into your household vocabulary as soon as possible. We use Mommy-Daddy time. You can use that or come up with your own; however, it is good to have your time defined and real. Even on a regular night or a tough day when you just need to connect, take some Mommy-Daddy time. They will know it means quiet time without the kids for Mommy and Daddy.

With more energy from getting sleep again, having your room back to *your* room, and the ability to lock the door as you need to, you can work on bringing romance back in. Your Massage Tool works well here. Very easy to employ. "Hey hon, why don't you come sit between my legs and let me give you a neck rub?" BOOYAH. Give to get, my friend, give to get!

The next tool you are about to learn changed my life.

 ## THE TOOL IS THAT A LOVER LISTENS!

As we move from phase to phase and as life keeps changing on us, we change. You will change and so will your partner. That means her needs as well as yours will evolve. Every day we see advertisements of what sexy is supposed to be. The truth is that you do not need to have a six-pack to be a good lover—you just need to help your woman climax, and six-pack abs are not what will make that happen.

ASKING HER WHAT SHE NEEDS EMOTIONALLY AND PHYSICALLY, ACTIVELY LISTENING TO HAVE A CLEAR UNDERSTANDING, AND THEN WORKING AS HARD AS YOU CAN, BEING OPEN TO LEARNING NEW SKILLS IF NEED BE TO GET IT DONE IS WHAT IT TAKES AND WHAT WILL MAKE YOU A HERO HUSBAND.

After some years of marriage, without realizing we were changing, Michelle began giving me some new feedback while in bed. I would definitely take issue when she would ask me to slow down, then speed up, and then do this and then do that. I would think to myself, *We have never had any issues before when it came to getting the job done, so thanks for the input, but no thanks.* People change—her needs were changing even though I did not want to hear it. To her credit, she was letting me know what she wanted. It then came to me—I realized, why not just listen? And oh my God, wouldn't you know it? My job got a lot easier, and she became much happier! If you can control your ego—which is not the easiest task for many of us—and simply listen, you will help her get there more quickly and easily, all without six-pack abs! That's a guarantee.

One last bonus tool for you to help increase your odds at more connecting and lovemaking is to take the TV out of your bedroom. You may draw the line here, but taking the TV out is a freeing experience. You two can connect without having to wait for commercials. Now that you have a baby, you will find that some peace and quiet at the end of the day will pay you both dividends. The quiet will increase your odds of hooking up with your wife and also getting a better night's sleep.

My disclaimer here for having no TV in the bedroom is that you will probably end up having more kids, and that is because, like all of the other new tools you have been learning, this works.

My friend, connecting and being intimate is one of the nicest perks of being married. Try not to fall into expecting your love life to be fantastic; it takes effort. As my father used to say, marriage is a choice you make every day. He was right, and that is for all aspects of your relationship. Make the choice to reengage, and you will be helping your world and the world at large to be a better place.

I BELIEVE IN MY HEART THAT IF THERE WERE MORE COMMITTED, MONOGAMOUS, HEALTHY SEX GOING ON, THE DIVORCE RATE WOULD GO DOWN, HUSBANDS AND WIVES WOULD BE HAPPIER, AND THAT WOULD MAKE THE WORLD A HAPPIER PLACE TO LIVE! AND THAT IS WHAT I WANT FOR ALL OF US.

CHAPTER 12

DAD'S HEALTH TOOLS

WHILE you do not need six-pack abs to be a Hero Lover or Hero Dad, your life will be greatly enriched if you have good health and enough stamina to keep up with your kids. Your next set of tools are to help keep you healthy.

LET'S FACE IT: FEELING LIKE CRAP AND BEING TIRED ALL THE TIME TAKES THE JOY RIGHT OUT OF MOST EXPERIENCES.

Being the Hero Dad and Hero Husband for your family are not exceptions. If you ever need motivation to focus on your health, your growing family can be that motivation, because they will be looking to you to set the pace.

A few words about the tools in this chapter. If you put these tools to work, they will work for you. When it comes to health, I find you can get to the truth of how to be healthy if you think about it from the perspective of being a human being and what a human being needs as an organism to be healthy, which always comes down to the fuel we choose to use and moving our body. These are a few key tools from ten years of helping people regain their health, and they could also help you to feel better, have more energy, and be healthier. You should also know these tools are not your run-of-the-mill tools. You may even roll your eyes when I share what these tools are. These tools are arranged in order of ease of incorporating them into your life, from the least amount of effort to the most.

The first area of your health that would be beneficial to improve is your energy. Your new baby requires energy, so if you can get your energy back, then you will be ahead of the game.

You might think and feel that you are tired and drained. Do you come home from a long day's work and feel pooped? What about your partner? Is she pooped also? You work so hard. You need to pay the bills; you want to have some balance in your life, to work in some fun. You want to be there for your friends and your family, you want to have time to play, and you are pushing so hard all the time. You are tired, your partner is tired, and you are about to add a whole bunch of sleepless nights to the mix.

YOU ARE FEELING DRAINED BECAUSE YOU ARE DRAINED. MORE SPECIFICALLY, YOUR ADRENAL GLANDS ARE MOST LIKELY DRAINED.

Without this being a whole science lesson, I'll briefly explain to you about your adrenal glands and why most of us are so fatigued. Chances are you, like me, are operating mostly in what is called fight or flight. From the minute you get up to the time you go to bed, it's go, go, go. When your body is operating under emergency stress conditions, that is considered fight or flight. Be it emotional, physical, or chemical stress, it has a real physical effect on us down to a cellular level. Besides just feeling drained, our energy stores and body systems that are supposed to produce the chemicals and hormones to keep us functioning are being depleted by our constant need to dig down deep and keep going until we get it all done. In the end, the energy we are getting from digging down deep is from your adrenal glands.

Your adrenal glands are little glands that control and regulate hundreds of chemicals and hormones in your body. Hundreds and hundreds of programs that keep your body running originate from your adrenal glands. Hormones and chemicals that are produced by your adrenal glands regulate weight gain, weight loss, sleep cycles, mood, inflammation control, and blood pressure, just to name a few. Your adrenal glands do give you adrenaline to give you superstrength in an emergency, but they also are responsible for your other aforementioned body systems. Just like when you are pooped and have a hard time doing your jobs, so are your adrenals.

You may start getting all kinds of symptoms, from fatigue and not sleeping well to negative thoughts, weight gain, even blood-sugar issues. You may end up going to the doctor, which could start a whole cycle of tests and medications that could have been avoided if you are in general good health without any diseases or illnesses. When it comes down to it, you are drained because you are always under a ton of stress. Sucking it up and dealing with everything drains your adrenals, which can cause a major negative ripple effect.

Fruits, vegetables, and clean, lean proteins supply us with the nutrients that we actually need to replenish our bodies, organs, and the glands that keep us functioning, including the adrenal glands.

THE FIRST AND EASIEST TOOL TO USE IS TO INTRODUCE A FEW SUPPLEMENTS TO YOUR DIET THAT YOU CAN GET ONLINE OR AT YOUR LOCAL HEALTH-FOOD STORE. MY FIRST SUGGESTION IS AN ADRENAL-SUPPORT SUPPLEMENT.

There are so many benefits to adrenal support. If you infuse your adrenals with the nutrients they need, your energy will start coming back, your body will start functioning normally, you won't be holding on to weight as much, and you will start sleeping better. If you want to be a hero, look into getting yourself and your wife some adrenal support. Adrenal support is a resource we have in our home all the time. Between four kids and work, we are constantly under stress, and it just plain helps.

The second supplement that I recommend is fish oil, which is a good omega oil that helps your cell structure. All stress ends up having an effect on us down to a cellular level. The pollution in the air, any fried food, cookies, treats, and anything with sugar creates inflammation in our body. A good fish-oil supplement will help decrease inflammation in your body and joints and is also believed to reduce the risk of heart problems. If your wife is not taking fish oil right now, it may be a good idea. Why? It will help her body on a cellular level, and in a fetus, it supports eye and brain development.

The last supplement I recommend are trace minerals that deliver just what it says, trace minerals from the earth that should be in our foods that we are typically missing.

Vitamins are okay, but we do not typically have any "vitamin deficiencies" in the Unites States of America, because most of the foods on the market are fortified with vitamins. Many times, it's the minerals and nutrients from fresh fruit and vegetables that we are typically deficient in.

If you are in relatively good health and incorporate a couple of these supplements, you will feel better. Supplements are super easy to add into your life; you just buy them and take them! And they can be especially helpful during the high-stress time of transitioning into parenthood.

The next tool I want to share with you takes a bit more effort, but don't freak out; it's just juicing! As I said before, with our modern lifestyle, there is no way to get all the fruits and vegetables that our bodies need to function optimally. Juicing is an easy way to get a ton of nutrients quickly and easily. You do need a juicer, which takes fresh, raw fruits and vegetables and presses them to homemade juice. There are many brands and models of juicers, ranging from seventy-dollar, simple juicers, to premium juicers complete with bells and whistles. In the end, if you invest in a juicer and use it even a little, or use it, stop, and start again, you can't go wrong having a tool at your disposal that can produce high levels of nutrients as quickly as adding one juice a day or a few a week.

My brother used to give me such a hard time about being a health nut before he started to get into shape. Now he calls me and says, "Oh my God, this juice is delicious!" He likes to put the juice in the freezer to make a healthy ice-pop snack. The thing about juicing is that you don't need to go crazy drinking vegetable juice all day long. Even a few weeks of drinking one serving of juice every day will help your general health noticeably improve. I always keep it simple and put in carrots, apples, cucumbers, kale, and lemon because they're readily available and are high-octane fuel. I'll warn you now that the juice does look gross! Depending on what you throw in there, it could be green with all kinds of weird colors in there.

When people tell me it's gross and they don't like it, I ask them to think of drinking vegetables in the same way they thought of kissing boys or girls when they were younger. You also thought that was gross when you were in the third grade, but you got over it. Why? Because it is good for you! Most good things in life take a bit of effort and are not always easy. With juicing, it is all about getting important nutrients quickly. Simply make one and slug it down.

The next tool that I'm going to share with you is yoga! I know, keep rolling your eyes! But let me share with you—it is incredible. There so many misconceptions about yoga. However, it's also becoming more mainstream for men every day. You don't have to be flexible or in shape to do yoga, which is the beauty of it. You can start from anywhere. If you're a totally stiff, nonflexible, nonexercising person, yoga meets you where you are to help get you started and moving your joints. If you do lift weights or do CrossFit or any kind of weight-bearing exercise, it can put a lot of stress on the joints.

Through my education and practice, I've been exposed to many exercise systems, both by doing them myself and interacting with patients who practice them. If I had to choose one exercise system that could work and be beneficial for all human beings, it would have to be yoga. The practice of yoga covers most of our physical needs for a regular, everyday human being. Yoga will systematically and gently develop your strength, flexibility, balance, and coordination. Yoga is about centering and promoting balance—it is hard to put into words all of the positive benefits of practicing even a little yoga—not to mention the super-toned instructors in tight little yoga clothes, which you would probably agree are better to look at than your grunting workout buddy.

You can find a convenient studio or try one of the many amazing online resources available today and save a bunch of money. Michelle and I do yoga in our house and subscribe to a website called YogaGlo.com. You can try this particular site for free and pick your level, duration, teacher, and the kind of yoga you want to do. If you're trying it for the first time, the key is to start off at your own pace and find the style that you like. The only side effect of doing some yoga is having more energy, more flexibility, more strength, and feeling more at peace.

And here is a great Hero Tool: do some yoga with your partner! Michelle and I do yoga together whenever we have the opportunity. It's great bonding when you do something positive and healthy together. Try asking your partner, "Hey, hon, why don't we do a little fifteen-minute, wind-down yoga at the end of the day?" What is she going to say? "No, I can't believe you want to do yoga with me, especially to wind down!" No, she is probably going to say, "Sure, let's try it!"

The last tool takes the most effort because you usually need to leave the house. You guessed it: a little cardio.

When it comes to heart-healthy cardio, make realistic goals. You do not have to run a marathon, half marathon, or even a 5K. Simply get out and start walking three to five days a week. You want to be able to walk around Disney with your kid on your shoulders without having a coronary! And if your wife is in the giving mood, you want to be able to make things happen.

Building up to walking a few miles takes no time, and all you need to do is walk out your front door and go. Ideally, you would use a heart-rate monitor so that you know if you need to raise your heart rate by walking faster. Walk a little and you will feel better and lower your blood pressure—that is how it works in human beings.

A few years ago, I was big into CrossFit, and I think it is an amazing system that develops real, functional strength. One day, I was not paying 100 percent attention during a movement and I tweaked a muscle in my leg. During the time I took to heal, it came to me: how strong do I really need to be? Seriously! Ask yourself that question. How strong do you need to be? If you are a regular person who is not going to compete in a physical fitness contest, but would like to be "healthy" in terms of being physically fit enough to avoid problems like diabetes and high blood pressure, and have enough energy to keep up with your kids and look good, you may be surprised to find that a lower-impact, easygoing system like yoga is more up your alley than the more popular, intense, joint-pounding systems.

Yoga will only add to your happiness and well-being, and of course, all I want for you is to be happy and healthy enough to do the things that you want with your children and in your life. Your kids are going to want to be picked up, and you can be sure your munchkin will want you to carry her on your shoulders. If you have a problem with your stomach muscles or don't have much strength because you never exercise, you are going to be worn out in a minute. And what about chasing after your toddlers, and when the time comes, teaching them how to ride a bike? You've got to run behind them and hold the seat to balance it. If you want to be able to do those things, just a little bit of exercise goes such a long way. If your health is poor, it's more difficult to live life and do the things that you love. This set of tools really comes from the heart. I hope you take the opportunity to be involved in your kid's and wife's lives and enjoy your own.

My hope is that you take advantage of some of these tools, because they are so easy to incorporate and they will make a huge, huge impact on your game!

CHAPTER 13

DAD'S RELAXING TOOLS

AT this point, you have a toolbox full of tools that can and will help you with having more energy and feeling better physically. But so much of fathering and husbanding is mentally and emotionally taxing. So here are my out-of-the-box tools for keeping you sane and not losing your mind!

As with my other relaxing tools, you will probably roll your eyes at these, but don't knock it 'til you try it. The game has changed now that you have a baby, and a new game takes new tactics. Roll your eyes if you may, but these tools work, my friend, from the beginning until your kids get older. Just like the health tools, these relaxing tools are in order of ease of incorporation into your busy life.

If you were rolling your eyes at yoga, prepare to laugh out loud at this first tool: taking a hot bath.

 RELAXING IN A HOT BATH IS AWESOME FOR STRESS RELIEF AND RELAXATION.

You might be a shower guy. You might never have
taken a bath before! But life will get stressful—good,
but stressful. A hot bath at the end of the day is easy to
do, doesn't take a long time, and you are off to happy
land in no time flat. Why do you think taking a bath at
the end of the day is a "thing" for so many women? It
is a thing because it really does relax you and give you
an opportunity to mentally check out. If you're lucky
enough to have a tub with jets, as the kids get older
and are outside your room screaming and fighting, just

push that button. The jets come on, and bye-bye. Maybe you're lucky enough to have a tub made for two. Take a bath with your wife, talk about the day, connect, and relax. And here's another little bonus tool for you if you take a bath: throw in some Epsom salts, which soothe sore muscles and detoxify the body. You can get them from any grocery store or pharmacy. Just so you know, if you try Epsom salts, you will sometimes get a brown ring around the top of the tub. The brown stuff is not dirt, but the built-up toxins pulled out of your body. A nice, hot bath is an amazing tool to help you to chill out, and that's the name of the game. You want to survive this time? Then a hot bath helps whether you are a big macho guy, an MMA fighter, or an accountant—or an accountant who is an MMA fighter. The point is, if you are a human being that's holding stress in your joints and your muscles, a nice, hot bath will 100 percent help the cause of relaxing your muscles, body, and mind and help you fall asleep.

THE NEXT TOOL IS WORTH ITS WEIGHT IN GOLD: MEDITATING.

You might think that meditating is a little crazy or woo-woo, and it might be! However, meditating is proven over and over again to help increase your focus, immunity, mood, energy, mental strength, and patience, just to name a few of the many benefits[21] that will serve you for the rest of your life as a parent. Playing around with and exploring a meditation practice has been pivotal for me in increasing my self-control. There may be no greater tool than self-control when it comes to being successful as a parent.

Essentially, meditating comes down to sitting quietly and taking a few minutes to breathe and be present in mind and body. You do not need to be cross legged like a fancy yoga expert. All you need is to sit in a comfy position for you, whatever that may be. Then, slowly and consciously breathe—breathe in, breathe out.

I have been meditating on and off for three years now and more consistently this past year. Simply the act of stopping and taking a few minutes out of your crazy-busy day for yourself does wonders for your mental health. Start with one or two minutes a day, and slowly work yourself up to five, fifteen, twenty minutes, or however long you can steal away. Meditat-

---

21 Giovanni, "Scientific Benefits of Meditation – 76 Things You Might Be Missing Out On, Live and Dare, accessed December 7, 2016, http://liveanddare.com/benefits-of-meditation/.

ing is especially helpful in the beginning of parenthood when your baby is an infant and your routines are changing, because it gives you a few fleeting moments of calm. If you do not think that focusing on breathing calmly for a few minutes each day is important, let me share with you the story of the monk and his young student. A meditation student was talking to his monk, who was a master. "You know, this meditating really sucks!" he said. "What is the point of all this breathing? It's so boring!" The meditation master said, "I understand. You may be right that meditation is a big waste of time. Come to the edge of the pond. There is an exercise you may like better that will help you get the point."

They went over to the edge of the pond, and the master said, "Look at your reflection in the water." The student looked at his reflection in the pond, and the master placed his hand on the back of the student's head. Then, he dunked his head into the pond and held it there for a while. When he took his hand off and his student came up, the master said, "Do you think breathing is important now?"

MEDITATION HAS HELPED ME GREATLY TO FOCUS, INCREASE MY ATTENTION SPAN, AND MOST IMPORTANTLY, HAS HELPED ME DEVELOP MY SELF-CONTROL, WHICH HAS TRANSLATED INTO MORE PATIENCE.

Studies show you can start sensing benefits after twenty days, although personally I believe you can start seeing some real benefits sooner than that. As a father, partner, and new parent, you will soon find out what a significant role self-control and patience will play in your new world. Meditating is the best tool I have found to help develop these crucial skills, and I know you will be pleasantly surprised at what you have been missing if you try it for yourself.

The great thing about this tool is that you can put it into play today. When your baby and your partner are

sleeping, sneak away for a few minutes. Sit down in a comfortable position with a pillow under your behind or on a chair, put your hands softly in your lap, and breathe. Just do not do it in bed or you will doze off, which is great, but will not help you develop any skills. The effort to sit down and do the breathing makes the difference. Meditation will leave you feeling more focused, more energized, and a little more centered. I don't know who couldn't use a little more of that.

THE NEXT TOOL IS ONE OF MY FAVORITE STRESS-RELIEVING TOOLS: CHOPPING WOOD.

That's right, I am a fooler. First, I share with you taking a hot bath and meditating, and then your next tool is chopping wood. But as far as stress relief and mental relaxation go, chopping wood is right up there on the list. If you are a klutzy kind of guy, then you can try smashing a stump with a sledgehammer, which is just as effective and a little safer.

If you have even a small yard, get yourself an axe. My main axe is a Husky chopping axe that I got from my local Home Depot. I also got a really nice axe from Husqvarna, which makes power tools mostly, but this axe is right up there with a Gränsfors Bruks, a top-notch axe. Many of us sit at a desk or are behind the wheel of our car most of the day and are far removed from chopping wood.

LET'S FACE IT—WE LIVE IN A FAST-PACED, STRESSFUL WORLD, AND ADDING A BABY DOESN'T MAKE IT ANY EASIER, AND WE DO NOT OFTEN HAVE THE OPPORTUNITY TO LET OFF STEAM. SOMETIMES IT IS NICE TO SMASH STUFF IN A CONSTRUCTIVE MANNER.

If you are nowhere in the range of a stump to smash or tree to chop, get yourself a few used tires from a garage, bolt them together, and smash them with a sledgehammer.

IT IS SO RELIEVING TO GET OUT SOME OF THE PENT-UP IRRITATION WE OFTEN FEEL FROM TRAFFIC, JOB FRUSTRATIONS, AND GENERAL LIFE STRESS. ALL STRESS IS NOT BAD; HOWEVER, ALL STRESS HAS A PHYSICAL EFFECT ON US! SOME OF IT GOES INTO OUR MUSCLES. SOME PEOPLE GET ULCERS OR DIGESTIVE ISSUES. YOU WILL BE SURPRISED AT HOW GOOD YOU WILL FEEL IF YOU DO SOME CONSTRUCTIVE SMASHING, WHICH IS MORE EFFECTIVE THAN YELLING AT YOUR PARTNER OR CHILD FOR SOMETHING THEY WERE NOT RESPONSIBLE FOR. PLUS, YOU WILL ALSO FEEL PRETTY MANLY AND RUGGED, WHICH IS A NICE SIDE EFFECT.

My disclaimer here is that you should think safety, safety, safety. Before you start wielding your axe, Paul Bunyan, get yourself some safety goggles, and I recommend some steel-toed shoes, which are both less expensive than getting your foot reattached or getting a bionic eye.

Last but certainly not least of these relaxing tools is a sense of humor. When your adorable little angel throws her sippy cup and shatters your flat-screen, when your son drops your cell phone in the toilet to see if it will float, when your little buddy decides to Sharpie your white leather couch, remember . . . humor!

Being able to laugh, relax, and destress will come in very handy in your coming years. These are just a few tools that work for me and could work for you as well.

CHAPTER 14

THE JOURNALING TOOL

TO introduce you to your next Hero Tool, let me ask your perspective on a few ideas. Do you think that your life is defined more by the major events, like your wedding day and the day your baby will be born? Or is it defined by the day-to-day words, thoughts, feelings, and actions that surround the big events? Do you think that your life has been moving fast up to this point? Do you think introducing a new baby into your world is going to slow things down, or speed time up? If you believe how you treat people and what you say and do every day is more defining than the major events, and if you think that time is moving quicker and quicker, then we are in agreement.

If you are reading this BC (Before Children), you are actually in the calm before the storm. Once your baby comes, time will start moving even faster than before.

 THERE ARE GOING TO BE SO MANY DAY-TO-DAY, AMAZING MOMENTS THAT ARE FUNNY, HEARTWARMING, SCARY, AND EXCITING THAT IT IS VIRTUALLY IMPOSSIBLE TO REMEMBER THEM ALL. THESE AMAZING, DAY-TO-DAY MOMENTS ARE LIKE FOOTPRINTS IN THE SAND—HERE ONE MOMENT AND WASHED OUT BY THE TIDE THE NEXT.

You may not believe this, but I have found a tool that will help you capture many of the small moments as well as slow down and even go back in time so you can remember and appreciate moments that would otherwise be lost. Like several of your other tools, which you initially rolled your eyes at, this one also will prove to work like a charm and be worth its weight in gold. The tool to slow down and travel through time is journaling. Keeping a journal is the answer to remembering some of the amazing, everyday moments that will otherwise be lost forever through the different stages of your new journey. There are many, many benefits to journaling about events and everyday thoughts and feelings you experience in your life. If you feel that nothing that exciting or worth documenting has happened to you up to this point, having your baby will certainly change all of that.

Here are three good reasons to journal. First of all, considering the amount of data you need to process on a daily basis when you're a new parent, it's amazing your head does not explode. Keeping a record can help you to remember the small moments that stand out to you, like the time Lila was fourish years old and we were in line at the deli counter, and out of the blue, she looked at the lady standing right next to us and said, "Did you know that my dad likes to sleep naked?" Everyone including the lady behind the counter got a chuckle out of that one.

Not only does journaling help you remember small moments, it also helps you remember how you were feeling or what you were thinking at different stages in your life. What were you thinking when you found out you were going to be a dad? How did you feel then? How are you feeling now? It is nice to periodically go back and remember thoughts and feelings, and see how you have changed.

Second, journaling could help with your marriage. Now that we've talked so much about the importance of sharing our thoughts and feelings with our partner, having a place to write some of them down really helps to get them out more clearly, which can help to avoid conflict. A journal is a safe place where you can put your feelings down without being criticized or interrupted, and it is amazing how you can get your thoughts and ideas organized and clear by having them to look at instead of having them bouncing around in your head.

Lastly, your journal can be a time machine for you. If you keep a journal, years from now, as life marches on, you can come back and be transported in time and space to an experience in your life. You can literally feel the feelings you did all those years ago, like the day your baby first said, "Daddy."

Just yesterday, a chilly February day, my boy Jonah and I were in the backyard. We lit a fire in the fire pit, threw some horseshoes, and then chilled out in the hammock for a little while. He said to me out of the blue, "Wouldn't it be nice if we remembered this day a long time from now?" And I said, "We will because I will write it down in my journal."

Before we wrap up this Journaling Tool, I am going to share with you two other meaningful events that I recorded as examples of a few of the many benefits of keeping a journal.

The first one I would like to share is from August 27, 2002. This was about five months before my first daughter Eliana was born. The entry reads:

HI, BABY. I'M SO EXCITED TO BE YOUR DAD. I LOVE YOU ALREADY, AND ONE DAY LONG FROM NOW, WHEN YOU READ THIS ENTRY, I WILL HAVE WATCHED YOU GROW FROM A BABY TO AN ADULT, HOPEFULLY. HOWEVER, RIGHT NOW, RIGHT THIS MINUTE, YOU ARE A TINY BABY IN MOMMY'S BELLY. I COULD FEEL YOU KICK AND I WONDER WHAT IS GOING ON IN THAT BELLY RIGHT NOW. I WILL BE A GOOD DAD TO YOU. I'LL BE HONEST AND TEACH YOU ABOUT LIFE AND LISTEN TO YOU. I'M SURE IT WILL NOT BE SO EASY AT TIMES, HOWEVER, I PROMISE TO DO MY BEST. MY HOPE IS THAT WHEN IT'S MY TIME TO GO, YOU AND HOPEFULLY YOUR SIBLINGS WILL READ THROUGH MY JOURNALS AND SMILE AND BE ABLE TO SAY I DID A GOOD JOB BEING YOUR DAD.

I never said I was Shakespeare, okay? That's the beauty, though—you don't have to be anyone but yourself in your journal.

Because this is all about being a dad and becoming a father, this next entry is especially meaningful to me because it is about my dad. I wrote this after he passed away to read at his funeral. Don't worry; it is not all that sad. I do remember sitting in my mom's kitchen, writing this in my journal and knowing I was going to speak at his funeral, which was October 7, 2003.

MY FATHER ALWAYS TOLD ME THAT I TALK TOO MUCH AND HE WAS NOT FOND OF LISTENING TO SPEECHES UNLESS THEY WERE HIS OWN, SO I'LL MAKE THIS SHORT. EVERYBODY HERE WAS LUCKY ENOUGH TO KNOW MY FATHER. I THINK IF WE ALL COMPARED NOTES ABOUT WHAT KIND OF MAN HE WAS, THE ODDS ARE THAT THE PICTURE WOULD BE CONSISTENT, AND IF MY DAD WAS ANYTHING IT WAS CONSISTENT— CONSISTENT WITH HIS VALUES, OPINIONS ON LIFE AND POLITICS, HIS GENEROSITY, AND PUTTING EVERYBODY BEFORE HIMSELF. MOSTLY HE WAS CONSISTENT WITH HIS LOVE FOR HIS WIFE, HIS

CHILDREN, GRANDCHILDREN, FAMILY, AND THOSE AROUND HIM. MATERIAL THINGS WERE NOT IMPORTANT TO DAD. IT WAS FAMILY THAT WAS MOST IMPORTANT. HE TAUGHT US ABOUT BEING GOOD HUMAN BEINGS, HOW TO TREAT PEOPLE, HOW TO TAKE CARE OF A WIFE AND A FAMILY, AND ESPECIALLY HOW TO CARE FOR A WIFE AND TO KEEP HER HAPPY. WE ALL KNOW THAT WAS IMPORTANT TO DAD, AND THE REASON THESE THINGS ARE PART OF WHO I AM IS NOT BECAUSE HE TOLD US HOW TO DO THESE THINGS, BUT BECAUSE HE SHOWED US HOW TO DO THESE THINGS BY EXAMPLE. DAD'S CONSISTENCY, LOVE, AND HUMOR WERE LARGER THAN LIFE AND HAVE ALWAYS BEEN AN ANCHOR FOR ME AND ALWAYS WILL BE. I LOVE YOU, DAD. LIKE THE SALT OF THE EARTH, I LOVE YOU.

Going back and reading through these lines transports me to that moment every time. I do not know much, my friend, but I do know that there is no way I would have remembered what I said at my father's funeral if I had not written it down.

Tony Robbins says that "a life worth living is a life worth recording." Experiences that will span every emotion that you have are going to come up now in your life as you begin to raise your new baby. You will do things, say things, and feel feelings that you have never experienced before, things you are going to wish you could remember in thirty years, ten years, or even next year.

FIND A METHOD THAT YOU LIKE. MAYBE THAT MEANS A PHYSICAL JOURNAL WHERE YOU GET TO PUT PEN TO PAPER, OR MAYBE YOU WOULD PREFER TO PUT YOUR FINGERS TO THE KEYBOARD OR MAKE VOICE RECORDINGS. NO MATTER THE VEHICLE, IF YOU MAKE THE EFFORT AND RECORD YOUR JOURNEY, EVEN SOME OF THE GOOD BITS AND PIECES, YOU WILL HAVE AMAZING STORIES TO SHARE WITH YOUR KIDS AND GRANDKIDS.

CHAPTER 15

THE BAND-AID TOOL

ALL right, my friend, we are nearing the end of our time together, and I want to share with you an ultimate Hero Tool that my father passed to me. This last tool is guaranteed to make you a hero time and time again. This tool falls under the category of health and safety, but it is important enough and will prove itself worthy enough to be in its own category. The tool is to always, from this day forward, keep a few Band-Aids in your wallet.

You will come to find that for children, a Band-Aid is like a magical cure-all that does more than cover up a boo-boo. It has the amazing power to cover them with a blanket of security that says you have the situation under control. You will see how amazingly a Band-Aid works to help your small children to feel better from minor cuts and boo-boos.

There will be numerous opportunities for you to shine by having a Band-Aid in your wallet, more than you will be able to count. You will save the day with

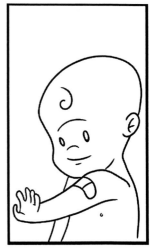

your kids, as well as for scores of children around your community. You see, you will be able to swoop in and save the day while you are at a play date, at the park, or at the local playground when your or some other little kid will fall off the swing. You can be that dad that goes up to that parent who is trying to soothe their crying kid's scraped knee with a hug, and you get to say the magic words, "Would you like a Band-Aid?" The skies will clear and you will see a crying child smile as they give you this amazing, approving nod, and you will have saved the day. You get to walk away knowing that that you helped that little child feel better, as well as knowing that the mom or dad is thinking to themselves, *Wow, what a real Hero Dad!*

That is a good feeling to have.

CHAPTER 16

CREATING AND COMMUNICATING YOUR VISION

MY friend, we have now spent so much time together. You have a whole toolbox full of tools and strategies to help you survive the early stages of bringing your infant home and to thrive during the phases that will follow.

This final tool will help you bring it all together when it comes to sharing your life with your partner and introducing your baby into that life. The tool is to have a vision, or at the very least a big-picture idea of how you want to see your life unfold. Knowing what you want from your next chapter as a father will increase your odds of being the dad you want to be, as well as increase your odds of maintaining a healthy marriage.

Here's why. You and your partner grew up in two different homes with different experiences, holiday traditions, and crazy relatives, and that is great. While you have melded your lives so far and may have had to negotiate whose parents' house you go to during the holidays and what movie to rent on Saturday night, a lot of new issues

are going to come up now that you're having a baby.

You have heard me say this before, and here it is again: Granted that your baby is healthy, your baby will not be the stressful part about having your baby. Seriously, managing your infant will not be difficult. It will be tiring, for sure, but changing poopy diapers and handling a bottle feeding are not difficult tasks once you know what you are doing, and by now I'm sure you do.

The stressful part about having your first baby is that all of your daily and life routines are about to change. Your relationship with your partner is about to change. Change is often difficult to deal with in general. If you do not know what you want or how to speak up about it while the new normal for you and your partner is being created, then you risk not continuing old family traditions, sharing fun experiences from your childhood, and making positive new experiences you want to see unfold. The other risk is coming home one day down the road and finding yourself in an unhappy situation that you helped to create because you chose not to communicate.

RIGHT NOW, YOU ARE CONCERNED WITH SURVIVING THE FIRST COUPLE OF MONTHS, WHICH IS COMPLETELY JUSTIFIED. HOWEVER, HAVING A VISION OF THE FUTURE IS ULTIMATELY JUST AS IMPORTANT, BECAUSE KNOWING HOW YOU WANT THINGS TO BE IN THE FUTURE WILL DICTATE HOW YOU NEED TO ACT TODAY AND TOMORROW TO MAKE YOUR VISION AND DREAM A REALITY.

What we are going to cover now is the 5 to 10 Percent Communication Tool. Then, we are going to cover tools that will help you to clarify your vision.

Men are famous for being great at many things; however, communication is not typically at the top of the list. You do not need to become the most proficient communicator on the planet, although you should know that in general, the more you share with your partner and the less you hold inside, the more you will increase your odds at creating a long-term successful marriage and family. This is because our partners are not mind readers, and as much as we would like them to, they do not know what we want unless we communicate it. The more you share about what your wants and needs and feelings are, the more she should want to share, which will increase both of your odds at getting what you want. In turn, that increases the odds of you being happier and building more trust, which builds the foundation for a lifelong partnership.

Let's say, though, that you are a quiet guy and not the best at sharing what is inside. That is where the 5 to 10 Percent Communication Tool comes into play. You will not be called upon to communicate your deepest feelings every day. However, when you two start making decisions on pediatricians, vaccinations, pre-

LISTENING BASICS

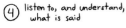

schools, and other important matters, that is when you need to chime in. Those issues represent the 5 to 10 percent of choices that are not routine and are important enough to speak up about. If all goes well, many of your everyday decisions will be about 90 percent routine, which you can decide to be involved with as much as you want. I say the more the better, but again, if you are a quiet guy and you and your partner are okay with them handling much of the typical daily routine and that is what you two have worked out and decided on, then just remember that when the 5 to 10 percent comes up, you need to speak up about it.

How do know what the 5 to 10 percent of issues that really are important to you are? Great question! You know by clarifying what your vision is and what you want to make sure happens while raising your baby. When you know that, you will feel when the important stuff to you comes up.

A vision is one tool that absolutely will increase your odds of success in becoming the father you want to be and having the life that you want to live.

Having a short-term vision, like getting through the next couple months, as well as what you want things to be like five years down the road, enables you to figure things out while keeping on track. It also enables you to get back on course if you lose your way, which happens to the best of us.

If you do have a vision of what you want, then it is simply a matter of speaking up. Let's say you do not have a vision. If not, it is time to figure out what your vision is so that you can participate in shaping your child, family life, and home.

Many men from class say that they had amazing dads and wish only that they will be half the man and father that their father was. You can be, but what is *your* plan? Your vision of how to be the great dad your father was? And what's your twist on the job, making you even better than your dad? What did he do that you want to emulate, and what do you want to improve upon?

Not every man plans on being such an involved father. I will share with you that there is no limit to the amount that you can be involved in your child's life, and the more involved you are, the better your kid will turn out to be. Take a little time and define what you want in order to make it happen. Maybe you had a great dad and maybe you did not. This is a real opportunity to change history for your next generation.

If your dad was crap, then your first tool is a list of what you will do differently. Listen more, show more emotion, be around more—make your list and share it with your partner. Your odds will go up of making it happen. It is not enough just to say that you want to or will be different. You need to identify the specific areas you want to improve upon and be conscious of them so that you will be better prepared to insert your evolved behavior when it is appropriate. You will at least be able to identify when you act in a way you would like to change and do better the next time. It is not always easy to break behaviors that we learned as kids. That is why making a list and being conscious is a good start.

Your second tool in creating your vision is to start with the end in mind. Think about how you want to be remembered by your kids and grandkids when you are seventy-five. What do you want your kids to tell their kids about you? What do you want to teach your kids, and what do you want to show them or expose them to? What traits or skills do you have that are uniquely yours that you want to make sure you pass on to your kids? Do you want discipline enforced in your home? What style of parent do you want to be? Do you want to raise self-sufficient kids who will need to do chores and help around the house to teach them responsibility? Or will you be more of the do-everything-for-your-kids-so-that-they-don't-have-to-do-work-around-the-house-style parents? There is no right or wrong. It is about knowing what direction you want to move in so you can contribute to the navigation of your family.

If you want your kids to be reminiscing about their childhood with some friends when they are adults and for them to say that you were an involved and awesome dad, then think about how you'll make it happen. Write it down and share your vision with your partner. What is your partner's vision? Does she have one, or are you both planning on making it up as you go along? If you haven't already, ask her about her vision and then come up with your family vision together so you can tell if you are on track as a family. If you do not know where you want to go, how are you two going to get there? It is one thing for you two to be lost out on the sea, but do you also want your baby to be adrift?

When you figure out what you want, she figures out what she wants, and you both share what you want with each other, you eliminate or at the very least decrease potential issues by creating the page that you want to be on together. If you choose to not share your vision as your new baby enters your life and home, you risk coming home one day to a kid who has traits that you do not like and a home life you are not happy with.

IT HAPPENS EVERY DAY. LACK OF COMMUNICATION IS ONE REASON THAT THE DIVORCE RATE IS SO HIGH. IT WILL BE DIFFICULT FOR YOU TO DEFEND YOUR POSITION OF WANTING CHANGES IN HOW YOUR KIDS ARE BEING RAISED IF YOU NEVER STAND UP FOR WHAT YOU WANT TO SEE BECAUSE YOU DIDN'T TAKE THE TIME TO FIGURE OUT WHAT YOU WANT, NEVER COMMUNICATED OR GOT INVOLVED, AND THEN DECIDED LATER THAT YOU WANTED CHANGES MADE.

It is not impossible to remedy that situation, although it is a lot easier to avoid that situation entirely. In the end, if you are in a healthy relationship and you both communicate what you want your family to be like, you will get some version of a compromise. However, that version will be a lot closer to what you want if you have an idea about what you want and speak up.

I SAID IT ONCE AND I'LL SAY IT AGAIN: MARRIAGE IS A CHOICE THAT YOU MAKE EVERY DAY. EVERY DAY, YOU CHOOSE TO RECOMMIT AND ENGAGE WITH YOUR WIFE AND KIDS. IT IS EASIER TO DO THAT IF YOUR WORLD IS ONE YOU WANT TO LIVE IN, AND THAT IS UP TO YOU STANDING YOUR GROUND ON THE IMPORTANT ISSUES, BEING OPEN TO COMPROMISE, AND ALWAYS WORKING TOGETHER WITH YOUR PARTNER TO REACH YOUR GOALS. THESE WILL DRAMATICALLY INCREASE YOUR ODDS OF SEEING YOUR SHARED VISION HAPPEN.

CLOSING
THOUGHTS

WE have reached the end of our time together, my friend. You can be the dad you want to be, no matter where you came from. You have the power to create the fathering experience and marriage you want. If you invest in being a good husband and father and work together with your partner to build a successful family, you will have an amazing foundation to build all your other success around.

The tools presented here to you work and can help you. But the thing about tools is that you have to use them. Be brave. You do not need to use every tool. Pick a few tools and put them into play. Like Henry David Thoreau said in the conclusion of his book *Walden,* "If one advances confidently in the direction of his dreams, and endeavors to live the life which he has imagined, he will meet with a success unexpected in common hours."

My wish is that you feel motivated and more prepared to embrace your new role as a father. I wish that your partner has a healthy and safe delivery and you are blessed with a healthy child.

I wish that your new family will experience only small boo-boos, wealth enough to always have the necessities in life, happiness with small valleys to help you appreciate the peaks, and the foresight to record your journey, because it goes so unbelievably fast.

If you enjoyed this book and you feel *Hero Dad* has been helpful, please recommend it to the future Hero Dads that you know. Visit the Hero Dad website at TheHeroDad.com, where you will find helpful videos as well as cool and useful gear. Thank you for spending this time with me. Congratulations! Now go become the Hero Dad in your home!

ABOUT THE AUTHOR

Dr. Yale Nogin has been teaching and preparing men for the successful transition into fatherhood and husband-hood (with baby version) for the past fourteen years.

He is an expert in the skills necessary to create a fatherhood experience grounded in being relevant & respected as a man, husband and father which lead to living in a relaxed home environment. He believes these are the ideal circumstances to live a healthy, fulfilled life with a partner while raising children.